# THERE WAS A TIME

MY FATHER AND ME OUTSIDE THE SHOP
IN WHICH I WAS BORN

*Walter Greenwood*

# THERE WAS
# A TIME

JONATHAN CAPE
THIRTY BEDFORD SQUARE LONDON

First published 1967
© 1967 by Walter Greenwood

T

1002540079

Printed in Great Britain
by Ebenezer Baylis & Son Ltd,
The Trinity Press, Worcester, and London
on paper made by John Dickinson & Co. Ltd
Bound by A. W. Bain & Co. Ltd, London

# Contents

# *Illustrations*

*There was a time when meadow, grove and stream,*
*The earth, and every common sight,*
*To me did seem*
*Apparelled in celestial light,*
*The glory and the freshness of a dream ...*

WORDSWORTH: Intimations of Immortality

*to my parents and my sister*

# I

# *A Gradely Lad*

On the 18th day of May in the year 1900 a handsome thirty-two-year-old bachelor removed the barber's pole from its angle-iron above his shop, fixed a large Union Jack to it, then, with flag waving, marched off to visit each of the eight public houses in the street and got gloriously drunk. On December the seventeenth 1903 he, now married, made the flag-waving tour once again. The first occasion was to mark the Relief of Mafeking, the second to proclaim the arrival of his first-born — me.

My mother considered this sort of behaviour low-bred and undignified, an opinion Father found peculiar and rather mystifying. While being anything but unfriendly she, as a general rule, disapproved of standing with groups of neighbours exchanging tittle-tattle in the street. Father, on the contrary, loved, when waiting for custom, to stand in his shop doorway or sit on a chair on the pavement and greet all who passed with a cheerful wave and jovial comment. Furthermore, being what is now called an extrovert, he liked to set things going rather than wait for them to happen, as on that summer evening when, trade being slack and Mother absent shopping, he decided that things, locally, needed enlivening.

In the early part of the nineteenth century and on Kersal Moor, which is three miles or so to the north-west of where we lived, it used to be the custom for races to be run, naked men being the contestants. This, Father insisted, was to give the girls a chance to weigh up form. I do not know if the remembrance of this report prompted my father but, surveying all us children in the street, he proposed a race in the nude to the top of the street and back again, the winner to receive the prize of one halfpenny. The enthusiasm of the competitors was complete. In no time we were naked, unashamed, lined up and away at the 'Go' signal. Halfway back to the finishing line my mother walked round the corner. Her children, naked, racing publicly with others in like state, her husband excitedly cheering his entries on while other neighbours bawled encouragement to theirs! She sought the support of Father's chair standing on the pavement. She sat down and fainted as the winner crossed the line. It was then that Father saw his wife and her condition. 'Brandy,' he shouted, with commendable presence of mind, 'brandy,' and waved his hand to the publican who was standing in the pub's doorway across the street. The glass was passed to my father who, raising it to his lips, drank it off. 'There,' he said, 'she ought to feel better after that.'

The company of his fellow men was imperative to his ebullient nature and this need urged him, all too frequently, into any one of the pubs which then were open from five thirty of a morning until eleven at night.

'Rum and Coffee 3d.' the cards said in the pub windows, and these were addressed to the clattering, clog-shod multitude on its way to mill and factory for the daily twelve hours' shift. The delectable mixture was, everybody knew, a specific for the chronic coughs and chest complaints that were endemic. It had another quality, that of making some of the inbibers deaf to the imperious discordance of factory sirens that shook the morning air at six o'clock. The few who succumbed were those who found the prospect of twelve hours' unrelieved toil intolerable and who knew that the pubs' open doors offered the 'quickest way out of Salford'.

The hangovers which followed Dad's fallings from grace did not, understandably, put him in the mood to welcome wifely reproof. 'Yes, yes,' he snapped, to my mother's strictures, 'I know I'm a damned fool but there's no call for you to rub it in,' then, histrionically: 'From now on we'll turn over a new leaf.' He took a penny from his pocket and gave it to me. 'Seidlitz powder from the corner shop,' he said, adding, 'then nip round to the Temperance Hall and get me a Pledge Form.' This was a certificate, printed in blue, attesting that he or she who signed on the dotted line promised never again to touch alcohol in any form. Father signed this with a great flourish and it was added to the collection.

He tried, without success, to convince my mother that his visits to the pub were 'for the sake of business'. She reminded him that only the publican and brewery appeared to be the beneficiaries. When sent to bring him to attend a customer I never had the slightest difficulty in tracking him down. All I had to do was to find a pub resounding with laughter and this told me that he was there and was the cause of the merriment. The risqué tales that kept his customers on a roar were also, in Mother's view, 'low-bred and undignified'. Out of consideration for her sensibilities when thus entertaining his customers he closed the door separating shop from kitchen. At this, Mother put aside whatever she happened to be doing, opened the door an inch and added her muffled laughter to that in the shop.

Both his parents had died long before I came upon the scene. His father was a Yorkshireman from Halifax which, too, was my father's birthplace and that of most of his brothers and sisters. His mother was a Welsh lady from Wrexham and it was from her, I suppose, that he inherited his black hair, histrionics and his excellent bass-baritone voice. He met his bride-to-be at the wedding of one of his sisters to a brother of my mother's. At this time my parents were in their early thirties and, I think, Mother was impressed at the wedding reception by the attentions of the dark-eyed, gay caballero of whom she then knew nothing other than that he was full of life and delighted the company with his bravura singing.

Biographical scraps of his earlier days were sometimes dropped by neighbours who called in on Mother for a chat. I eavesdropped from my listening post under the table. One neighbour, who was particularly welcome, was a widow of my mother's age named Polly Mytton. She always had a fresh-scrubbed and laundered look about her; even the dome-headed brass nails of her clogs were polished. She scratched a precarious living from the sale of home-made crumpets and pikelets which she trundled round the streets in a small box-truck on three cast-iron wheels. She announced her wares by ringing a brass hand-bell, then singing:

'Crumpets and pike — lets, four a pen — ny.'

In spring and summer she hawked bottles of dandelion and burdock and other drinks made from herbs she had gathered from the distant fields. Her companion on this occasion was a tall, hefty neighbour named Annie Boarder whose luxuriant black hair was held in place by a fan-shaped comb reminiscent of those worn by Spanish ladies. Her shawl was draped loosely on her broad shoulders, her muscular forearms uncovered, and these, together with her dark, bold eyes and booming voice, gave her a formidable and commanding appearance.

'We've come begging, lass,' she said after Mother had invited them to be seated. 'Wreath for Ben Lindsay. Though if it was left to me his wife'd have the money and bedamned to the flowers.'

'Annie Boarder!' Polly said, scandalized.

Mrs Boarder looked at Mother as one asking for sympathetic understanding. 'Hark to her.' She then stared severely at Polly: 'She's a widow woman now, isn't she? Seven kids to feed and not a blind penny compensation from them at the docks. Ben Lindsay's own fault, that's the verdict brought in. Own fault, is it? I tell you, those lawyers're hand in glove with the companies.'

'Poor woman,' Mother murmured, as she opened her purse. 'Nothing but trouble for some. However is she going to manage?'

'The best she can, like us all,' Mrs Boarder said. 'And if it was me I'd be round to that Board of Guardians double quick.' She put out her hand, palm upwards: 'In there.'

'Annie, Annie,' Polly said, reproachfully. 'The shame of it.'

'I could give you a good shaking sometimes, Polly Mytton,' Mrs Boarder declared.

'I'd die, Annie. That and the workhouse. I'd scrub floors, do *any*thing rather than see the day.'

'You great, daft loon, who wants to see the flamin' day? But when it's forced on you it's either that or singing in the gutter. Listen to us, though. Bedamned to trouble. Look on the bright side, that's me every time.' Laughter sounded from the shop: she smiled at Mother: 'Hark to him, that joker you married. Aye, he's a gradely lad. Made a fortune, he would, if he'd stuck to it. Now when he was Tom McCann —let's see, that'd be … Well, I don't suppose he'd be more than twenty-one.'

'Who?' Mother asked, perplexed.

'Tom Greenwood, o' course. That was his stage name. "Tom McCann, the singing Irish Comedian".'

'He never told me anything about this,' Mother said, her brows arched.

'He never told his ma and pa, neither. And they never would've found out if they hadn't've bought tickets for his benefit concert. As soon as he came on the stage his dad was on his feet. "It's our Tom" he shouts and off he and his missis went to the stage door and copped him when he came out with the money. Drunk for a week, the lot of 'em, till it was all spent. Ay! Happy days.'

'He's a fool, that's what he is where money and drink is concerned,' Mother said.

'Maybe,' Polly said. 'But he's given me and a lot more many a laugh and we've all got our failings. The best day's work that lad in there ever did was when he married you, lass.'

Mrs Boarder got up and arranged her shawl. 'Come on, let's get on with it, Polly, we haven't got all day.' She moved to the door, Polly following. 'Well?' Mrs Boarder said, stopping and looking at Polly. 'Aren't you going to ask her? See?' she added, looking at Mother. 'She's forgotten. It's old Mr and Mrs McBride.'

'Is there anything wrong?'

'Wrong? Ha! That'd be putting it mild. I wish you'd ask your father to call and see 'em. He might be able to help.' Throwing Polly a stern glance she jerked her thumb doorwards. 'And we don't want any moans and groans from you about them goin' in the workhouse.'

When they had gone Mother lifted the bob-fringed tablecloth and said: 'You can come out from under there, young man.' I was dispatched to my grandparents with the message. As I departed Mother called out after me, 'And watch out for the horses when you cross the road and come straight back.'

# 2

# *Pressures to Bear*

I saw my grandfather coming down the street. He went into the home of old Mr and Mrs McBride with one of whose grandchildren, Michael, I was playing. Michael's nickname was Mickmac. He was bow-legged, barefoot, scabby and one of a large family depending for its support on his father's casual labour at the docks. The sign that things were exceptionally hard for them was when my mother fetched out the biggest of our three brown earthenware hot-pot dishes, baked a huge potato pie in it, then took it to the McBrides' concealed under a towel in our laundry basket.

Mickmac and I sensed the air of doom from the subdued conversation of the women congregated on the pavement near old Mr and Mrs McBride's front door. 'The Grubber. My God, what an end.' The Grubber was the local name for the workhouse which, everybody feared, might be their ultimate place of residence.

Unobtrusively Mickmac and I sidled into his grandparents' home. The room was full of echoes, the only furniture was two chairs and the kitchen table, newspaper serving as table-cloth. The only wall decoration remaining was a crucifix: dusty outlines showed where pictures had been hung. A little red oil lamp with a bright reflector stood on the mantel. A string was stretched above the empty grate, and on this hung a pair of well-darned grey woollen socks and a white apron. The flagged floor had recently been scoured and the hearth-stone whitened.

Old Mr McBride sat in one of the chairs, both hands resting on his walking-stick: his wife was standing at his side, a hand comfortingly on his shoulder. They were motionless as though posing for a photograph.

My grandfather was at the table, dog-eared rent and insurance books in front of him. Mickmac's father looked on. A gaunt, broad-shouldered man, he was leaning against the wall, one leg crossed over the other, thumbs hooked in his belt which had a big, brass buckle. Mickmac's Aunt Theresa paced up and down jouncing her baby. She was a tall, strong woman and all the time she harped on what 'our Bridget' ought to do by way of helping the old couple. Mickmac was fond of boasting of his Aunt Bridget who, years ago, had gone to follow her trade of weaver to America where everybody was rich. 'She knows how we're all fixed here,' Theresa droned on, petulantly. 'You can't deny that, our Pat. Been written to weeks ago, she has—'

'All right, all right,' Mickmac's father said, irritably. 'Letters take time from America. Give our Bridget a chance, can't you? And you,' he added, spotting Mickmac: 'Who told you to come in here? Hop it. Go on, outside with you and play.'

We crept out and retired to our shop frontage. All matters of moment came up for discussion in our shop. Normally these concerned sporting affairs when the exchanges were flavoured with good-natured banter. That which followed Grandfather's appearance was bitter in the extreme. For me it was made more impressive by Mother's participation. She rarely trespassed on the men's conversations and I had never seen her so ardent and unrestrained. She looked at Mickmac's dad and said, incredulously: 'Do you mean to say your father won't get a penny back?'

Mickmac's dad made a restrained gesture towards my grandfather. He wore the perplexed air of one confronted with something beyond his understanding. 'That's what your dad said.'

'But ... Father,' Mother said, 'they've been paying weekly

on those insurances for thirty years.' She was staring with indignation.

'More than thirty years,' Pat McBride said. 'Shillin' a week. It's only since they stopped him workin' that he's missed payin'.'

My grandfather shook his head. 'The law's on the company's side. If the premiums aren't paid ... Well, there the scandal is. The policies lapse and the company benefits.'

'My Christ!' my father said. 'A shillin' a week for thirty years. Eighty quid and more. Why, the house he's living in cost less to build than that. Aye, and I bet he's bought that three times over with the rent he's paid.'

'It is outrageous,' Mother cried. 'It's barefaced daylight robbery. Poor old souls. Isn't it enough that the bailiffs have taken everything but the bed, a couple of chairs and the kitchen table? And now it's to be the workhouse.' Her indignant mood was shared by the group of women neighbours who had drifted to our corner, prominent among whom was Mrs Boarder. Her dark eyes were glowing and her fists were on her hips. Her opinion, forcibly expressed, obviously was not shared by our corpulent next-door neighbour Mr Wheelam. Because of his position of authority in the mills and because he owned property locally he considered himself privileged. Listening to the comments from his doorstep he said crabbily: 'I don't know what you're making all the fuss about, Annie Boarder. They'll be sure of a bed in the workhouse, won't they? They'll be clothed and fed, aye, *and* they won't have it to pay for. Poor Rate, that's where it comes from and property owners have to find for that.'

Mrs Boarder's eyes had been growing wider all the time he was speaking. 'Why ... ' she exploded, stopped and started afresh. 'Awaaay with you, you fat-gutted old bugger you.' Polly Mytton looked at her in alarm but the look was quite lost on Mrs Boarder who went on, furiously: 'You could say that for all o' them in Strangeways jail. Go and try it yourself for a couple o' months and take your soddin' rents with you. If I've got to starve I'll do it under my own roof and bedamned to the lot o' you.'

We did not see the old couple's departure. 'To Let' notices were stuck inside the blank windows of their house until a newly married couple took over when, in no time, a second-hand pram stood outside the door.

I had not seen the last of old Mr and Mrs McBride. Mickmac, on his way with a message to them, asked me to go with him. I knew what the message was all about since his father had made an agitated appearance in our shop with the news that Aunt Bridget had sent her parents five pounds from America. Dad advised Pat McBride not to let the workhouse officials know about the gift. 'If they have wind of it they'll collar every penny for their upkeep. You have 'em round to your place on their days out, Pat. Give 'em a slap-up dinner and a drop of the best till the money's gone.' Mickmac's message was to tell his grandparents to come for the initial treat.

The Salford Workhouse was a bleak barracks of a place whose row on row of uncurtained windows gave it desolating and forbidding air. Within were flagged, echoing corridors whose walls were of a glazed brown brick. Bare, scrubbed tables and benches furnished the common rooms. Fronting it, behind a high wall, was a wind-swept concrete yard divided down the middle by a run of spiked iron railings to segregate the sexes.

The women inmates wore a uniform of a blue frock reaching to the ankles, a grey shoulder shawl and a small hard bonnet held in place with elastic hooped round the bun of their hair. The men were shod in heavy boots, and wore suits of grey whipcord and black, broadbrimmed hats. When they walked abroad everybody knew their place of residence.

We stood with Mickmac's grandmother on her side of the railings, his grandfather looked down at us from the other.

After the message had been delivered we were blessed by the old couple and told that we were good boys.

My grandfather had prophesied that their committal to the workhouse was a death sentence. It was not long before Polly Mytton and Annie Boarder were doing the rounds collecting for the old couple's wreaths.

'There,' Dad said wryly after the obsequies. 'Slaved all their bloody lives, brought up a family, forked out for death insurance and they finish up with a pauper's funeral. Not that that'd trouble me.' He scratched his chin ruminatively, then held out his palm towards my mother: 'Come to think of it you can let *my* burial insurance lapse here and now and let's be having the pennies every week. If I sup it away in beer it'll be one in the eye for those insurance robbers ... *and* the right man will have benefited. Now what's wrong with you?'

My mother turned her head aside and closed her eyes. 'Such vulgarity.'

# 3
# *Parish and Ward*

For parliamentary and municipal election purposes our locality bore the name 'Parish and Ward of St Thomas, Pendleton'. Its church on the main highway to Liverpool, Bolton and the North occupies an island site, once the village green which had a maypole; but that, of course, was a long, long time ago when Pendleton was a fold of cottages and the green grass grew all around. It still has a Maypole but this is a pub.

The hideous face of the town under which the fields lie buried is of brick, the clay for which was dug out of the vanished meadows where once the skylark sang. The streets of tiny houses stand in straight lines shoulder to shoulder like soldiers on parade, one district merging into another without distinction, but each and every house representing to somebody the comforting place called 'home'.

In my childhood you did not need a calendar to tell the day of the week nor, of an early morning, a clock to tell the time. Work in the mills began at six o'clock. The silence of the sleeping streets was broken three-quarters of an hour before that by our district's 'knocker-up'. His name was George and he talked and sang to himself. He was aged, bearded and clogged and he carried a long pole tipped with wires which he rattled against his customers' bedroom windows. He addressed all the womenfolk by their Christian names and provided a daily weather report free of charge. When the hollow echo of his clogs did not resound through the empty streets you knew that the snow was deep or that his footwear was swathed with sacking to stop him slipping on the ice.

'Come on, there, Sair Ann. An' you'll need a pair of his old socks on thi clogs this mornin' unless you want to go crashin' on that big bum o' thine.' On to the next customer and another kettle-drum roll of wires against the window: 'Artow out o' bed, Mary Ellen? Get thi red flannel on this mornin'. There'll be snow afore this day's out.' Off he went singing: 'O ye Ice and Snow bless ye the Lord. Ooops! Whoa, there, nearly went down then, George lad. Take it easy. There's nowt in the canticle about praisin' and magnifyin' a broken leg.' Away he went, his singing of the *Benedicite* growing fainter. He was thoroughly versed in the services of the Church of England since he supplemented his income, and had done so for years, by pumping the organ in the parish church in whose organ loft he often went to sleep during the sermon. Aware of George's frailty the organist kept a choirboy, midshipman-like, on hand. If nothing happened after a chord had been struck the choirboy had to dart round the organ and shake George to wakefulness.

A rich member of the congregation put up the money for a motor to pump the organ. His kind offer was accepted but I do not think that the order for the motor was placed until the Order for the Burial of the Dead was read over George's earthly remains—though of this I am not certain.

When every street was hung with billowing washing, when the pawnshops were crowded at dawn with women, the day could only be Monday. Each Tuesday morn flocks of bleating sheep and herds of wild-eyed cattle crowded the roadways on their way to slaughter at the vast market near by. As the first mixed herd passed our shop Mother always rushed to the door, took a deep, shut-eye breath of the pervasive smell of cattle, then, with a profound cry from the heart, exclaimed: 'The country! Ah, the country!' Whereas my juvenile interest was in Mickmac and his ragged, barefoot counterparts— bottles, jugs and brew-up cans in hand, off to risk a drover's stick or a trampling, to milk the penned cattle.

Mid-week was signalled when, purses being empty or thin, either the gutterings of candles or the meagre glimmer of oil lamps supplanted the usual bright primrose gas-glow behind drawn paper blinds. This was the time when, with big shadows dancing on the kitchen walls, mothers fell to story-telling concluding with, 'That's all, kids. Off to bed, now. It'll soon be Friday and we'll have pennies for the gas.'

Love-sick swains had naught but sighs for comfort on Fridays, for this was 'bucket night', when dutiful daughters were put to the weekly chores scouring the house and, with emery-paper and elbow grease, were set the task of trans-muting steel fire-irons, fenders and the hinges and handles of oven doors into glittering silver. Younger brothers and sisters took turns bending over a newspaper spread on the kitchen table while mothers, with fine-tooth combs, hunted the undesirable crawlers known as 'bogies'. Then the tin bath was unhooked from its nail on the backyard wall and set in the middle of the hearth-rug when all were scrubbed and then put to bed.

For us who were young Saturday was the crown of the week. 'Spending money' was in our hands, the 'Saturday halfpenny' given with the warning: 'And, think on, you're not to spend it all at once.' Nor did we, since farthings were legal tender and sweets, at four ounces a penny, were sold and bought by the ounce. It was also the day of barrel organs and ragged beggars, vocal and instrumental, performing in the roadway. Everybody seemed to catch something of the day's cheerful and robust character, its air of carnival and the entertainment of shopping. Where the weekly roast was con-cerned the shrewd and thrifty housewives were aware that they had the butchers at a disadvantage. Refrigerators had yet to supplant ice boxes, and the customers knew that the butchers knew that if the stock were not cleared by closing time it would be rotten or have to be given away by Monday, when the dawn crush at the pawnshop told its tale of empty purses.

An hour or so before midnight while the pubs resounded with the uncertain harmony of tipsy vocalists, wives congregated outside the shops under the spluttering naphtha flares. It only needed one butcher to start for all to follow suit. Standing on the pavement, sometimes on a chair in front of the circle of upturned faces, he brandished aloft the unsold stock: 'Here y' are, ladies. Shoulder o' lamb — eighteen pence.' No response. 'Look. I'll throw in a couple o' breasts o' lamb — and what about this, liver and lights to go with it. Three shillings. What d'you say?'

'I say you must be mad. Think we're millionaires?'

'You're there, Annie Boarder.'

'I'm here.'

'It'll last you a week, won't it?'

'It'd have to. You chuck in that sheep's head and I'll give you half a dollar.'

'For Christ's sake give it her or we'll be here all night.'

Mickmac and other small boys lurking in the shadows by the baskets of vegetables on the pavements outside greengrocers', alert, organized, watching for the proprietor's attention to be diverted, then, with expert Rugby back-passes, flicking spuds, carrots and onions to fellow conspirators fielding in the gloom.

Tomorrow! Blessed day when from the open door of every house came the mouth-watering scent of 'the roast'. Music everywhere; gramophone records, drums and fifes of the Boys' Brigade on the march; solo performances by bandsmen who, shirtsleeved in front of a music stand under the parlour window, put in an hour's practice before sitting down to devour 'Sunday dinner', the one meal of the week from which all were certain to rise replete.

# 4
# *A Newcomer*

He was a few years older than me and a newcomer to the place. He was in charge of a rickety perambulator with buckled wheels which squeaked. A couple of babies of differing ages were within and these, I learned later, were given to a deal of screeching and howling. I also learned later that he was perpetually burdened with their care. This handicap accounted for his facial expression which was that of one permanently aggrieved.

His mother, a tough, raw-boned woman, took in the washing of the lower middle class to help support her large and ever-growing family. Her drooping, dispirited husband had a miscellany of jobs which included the door-to-door selling of the firewood he chopped, hawking fly-catchers in season, and taking bets from factories in the hope of a tip from a winner; he was also available as casual labourer to a local fish-and-vegetable salesman who hired out his pony and spring-cart to any debt-ridden householder forced to do a moonlight flit.

The newcomer's name was Nobby. He appeared at my side late one afternoon when I was alone. He wore girls' lace-up boots with high heels, picked up, no doubt, from the second-hand stalls of the market: his knickerbockers had patches on the seat and were frayed at the knees, as were the elbows of his jersey. His eyes were puffy from recent weeping and there was a reddish mark across his right cheek and ear where somebody had fetched him a clout.

He stopped the pram, looked me up and down warily, then, without preliminary, arched his brows and said, aggressively: 'An' I can pee further than thee.' Without waiting to learn whether or not the challenge was to be accepted he turned, took up position on the edge of the kerb and began to fumble with his flies.

This took place outside the front door of a Mrs Flarty. She was disliked by the neighbours because of her habit of back-biting. She was dumpy, swarthy, wore a man's cap and, with sweeping-brush in hand, was perpetually appearing on her doorstep on the look-out for somebody with whom to discuss other people's affairs. The objects of her malice were referred to not by name but by the number of their house: ' ... her at fifty-seven', ' ... them at ninety-six'.

After having looked up and down the street her glance fell upon the challenger who, knees bent, was charged and at the ready. She raised her brows, she raised the brush and, lunging, knocked Nobby off the kerb. 'Down the grid, you dirty pig,' she ordered, interrupting him when he turned to explain, 'and put it away while I'm talking to you. Another thing, back with you into your own street wherever it is.'

Pouting, Nobby buttoned up, sidled to the perambulator and began to pull it backwards in the direction of our shop. He looked yearningly at the lads of his generation larking on the plot of waste ground opposite. 'They won't let me play with 'em because o' this,' he mumbled and kicked the pram's wheels. His eyes brimmed and his lower lip took on a slight tremble. 'Can I help it if I've got to lug this thing about where'er I go?' He sniffed and ran the back of his hand under his nose. I could understand the boys' refusal to have him with them, handicapped as he was. Street games among the older boys demanded a quick getaway when police appeared. If they were collared it could mean a summons to court and a fine for 'obstruction'.

As he started to move away he looked at me and said: 'I'll let you come with me — if you want.'

'Where are you going?'

'I'm hungry,' he said, making three syllables of the adjective.

Daft-like, I thought him to be on his way to buy something. He confessed that, since the piece of fried bread at breakfast, he had not had anything to eat because, he explained, the lady whose washing he had delivered at midday had gone to Manchester and would not be home to pay until later that evening. 'Seven o'clock they said she'd be back and we're havin' fish and chips when I get the money, me mother said.' He added, '*All* of us.'

He got me to help pushing the pram until we stopped outside the iron gates of Blackshaw's works, a huge place buzzing with machinery and its clanging reverberations. I noticed Mickmac among the congregation of barefoot urchins waiting outside. When the siren blasted forth its deafening signal that work for the day was ended Nobby bossily instructed me to watch the pram. He joined the urchins as the gates were rolled back when a chattering, clattering river of oil-stained workmen and apprentices poured out. Immediately all the urchins held out their hands and began to chant a repetitive refrain: 'Any bread, cake or pie? Any bread, cake or pie?' Even when they were submerged by the flood their pipings still were to be heard. After the flow of home-going men had receded, the supplicants sauntered to the pavement feasting on left-over bits and pieces from midday meals.

Nobby had been out of luck. Possibly this was because he was bigger than the others and was not barefoot. Mickmac, seeing how matters stood, generously offered Nobby a share of his gains, then said: 'I know where we'll get summat. Mather's shop. Just be in time for the women comin' home.'

Mather's, a branch of a grocery chain, was in our street. It was crowded with clogged and shawled women buying bread and other necessaries. We joined the children lined up at its door. When a shopper came out, her apron bulging with loaves, the child at the head of the line asked, politely: 'Can I have your makeweight, please?'

To circumvent cheating on the part of bakers the Government had decreed that a loaf had to be sold by weight and, furthermore, it had to be weighed in the sight of the customer. If it did not tip the scales at the prescribed weight the shopkeeper had to cut a hunk from another loaf and add the balance, or 'makeweight'. When given the makeweight he or she at the head of the line of waiting children walked away munching and the next took their turn. That is, until we came to the queue's head, when Nobby organized things differently. Possibly assessing the pathos-value of Mickmac's bare feet he put him in charge of the pram, shoved me next to him and told us to take the collection. Having been given this he stopped us as we were about to give way to the others. 'You stay where you are,' he commanded. The other children raised objections to this unfairness but were subdued instantly by Nobby's savage threats. Every donation that came our way was stowed in the pram until, as the crush of women thinned in the shop, Nobby, giving Mickmac a scant share, ordered me to 'get pushin' ' and away we went to his home.

It was difficult to see his mother because of the steam vapour which clouded their small kitchen. A cast-iron cauldron full of clothes bubbled on the cross-bar of the grate. I could hear the fire roaring under the copper in the scullery. A tin bath heaped with scrubbed washing stood where the hearth-rug should have been and, under the window, was a mangle with worn rollers and a tin receptacle below to catch the water. There were a couple of wooden chairs and one that, at one time, might have been a rocker. The kitchen table, heaped with sodden clothing, was swimming with soapy water.

His mother's hair fell in damp wisps over her eyes. She pushed these aside with her forearm and looked at him dully when he pulled at her skirt, then showed her some of the bread we had collected. Mrs Clarke looked at it, let the scrubbing brush fall, slowly wiped her hands and forearms on her sacking apron and said: 'Ay, what a godsend, Tim. What a godsend.' She helped him to put the bread into the cupboard, passed him a stone jam-jar and, as she reached a squalling child from the pram added, 'Go to the corner shop and get a pennorth o' black treacle, lad.' She began to unbutton her blouse.

'You haven't given me the penny, Mam,' Nobby reminded her.

'Ay, Lord,' she murmured. 'Another penny. Heigh hi, ho.' She opened the rent book lying on the corner of the mantel-piece and took a penny from the coins inside. 'Here, lad,' she said, giving it to him as she flopped into a chair. She added, on a great sigh, as she began to suckle the child, 'And when you've had summat to eat don't forget to go round for the washing money again.' As we went out she began to sway to and fro crooning softly to the child.

# 5
# *Doctor's Orders*

---

The town's dark breath stained everything and cast its mournful shadow even on the workday clothes of all: dark suits for men, sombre-toned shawls 'that won't show the dirt' for girls and women. The shawl had an antique grace hanging in classic folds. The wearer, not being conscious of this, enhanced its charms. In later years, my head stuffed with omnivorous reading and, with particular reference to the works of William Morris and William Blake, I indulged myself with delights of an imaginary Salford, a place of clean air, the girls' and women's shawls of pastel shades and bright and cheerful colours.

As I write these lines the shawls have gone. Fashionable ladies for evening dress now wear the shawl's second cousin, the stole, of bright and cheerful colours.

The thick carpets of sawdust which were replaced daily on the tap-room floors of all the pubs, the brass spittoons which graced the bars' brass footrails, all attested to the prevalence of 'the English disease'.

My father was a chronic subject. His condition, like that of all his fellow sufferers, was aggravated, if not caused, by the incessant filth perpetually poured into the atmosphere by industrial and domestic chimneys.

All this borrowed its colour scheme from the devil's palette; dirty grey-blue from the houses, black billowing from the tall chimneys and, from the open windows of rubber works, heavy chemical vapours of a purulent yellowish-green that hung wraith-like on the air to drift slowly, burning into throats and lungs and painting a ghastly pallor on the faces of all who worked within.

When Father was attacked by a coughing bout it was well to keep out of his way. He damned it, he cursed it, he mopped his glistening forehead until, the bout subsiding, he flopped exhausted in a chair. Sometimes, in the small hours, I would start awake. There it was again, echoing horridly, and from below stairs came sounds of Mother kindling the fire and boiling a kettle to provide a hot and soothing concoction.

The doctor's advice, impractical in Dad's opinion, was removal of the business to the comparatively clean air in the vicinity of the public park.

'How many more times has he to tell you before you'll take heed?' Mother demanded.

'And how many more times do you want telling? My living's here. Customers won't follow us there.'

'If you go on here much longer with that cough of yours you won't be needing any customers at all.' She pointed at me. 'What's more, he's caught it.'

'Hell!' Dad muttered and went into the shop where the cough struck him again.

'Some people will not be told,' she called after him. 'And,' looking at me, 'as for you, young man, we'll have you along to the Children's Hospital and put paid to that cough of yours before it takes a hold. I wonder anybody's alive at all having to breathe this poisonous air. But we're moving, if it's the last thing I do.'

Already a preliminary step had been taken in that direction. Now that I was of age, instead of sending me to the local elementary council school attended by most of my playmates I had been enrolled in the Infants' Department of one newly built three-quarters of a mile away and adjacent to the public park. The lower middle classes and some well-to-do professional people had their solid homes round the park and, as a buffer between them and our rough and ready district, there intervened streets inhabited by those who would have been offended to be termed 'working class'. It was customary here for front doors to be closed when men returned from work, and their wives were not to be seen gossiping in friendly neighbourly fashion. The district had an inhospitable look, an empty air of bleak respectability.

Other considerations added to my mother's determination. Dad had dispatched a couple of rats slaking their thirst at the sink. Other unwelcome trespassers appeared in the form of a plague of blackbeetles. Mother, all guns blazing, presented herself at the Town Hall and demanded immediate action. Workmen came with picks and shovels, and took up the flagstones which paved our kitchen: there they were in shoals, blackbeetles, a moving, audible carpet of shining jet.

'And that, Tom Greenwood, is quite enough for me,' Mother declared. 'I have seen all I want to see of rats and blackbeetles. I know, I know,' she interrupted. 'I know quite well they aren't your fault and neither are they mine. There's an empty shop by the park and I'm going to see about it this very minute.' She disappeared upstairs, and presently, when she came down again, she was wearing her best dress of crushed-strawberry colour with shoulder-of-mutton sleeves, a hat trimmed with feathers round the brim and kept in place by hat-pins mounted with silver-finished acorns. She took our rent book which verified that she had never missed a week's payment and, without a word, off she stalked to see the house agent.

'Women!' Dad said to the ceiling when she had gone.

We moved to the new district after the shop had been fitted and made ready in optimistic expectation of the flow of new customers. For me the removal was banishment. Where were the resounding yells and shouts of the children at boisterous street games? These quiet empty streets were chill and daunting; they gave you a feeling akin to that when, having been dared in the public park, you sprinted over prohibited lawns and heard the blast of the keeper's whistle ordering you to 'Keep Off The Grass'.

Only once did I see any of my old playmates. These were Mickmac and Nobby, the former having been cajoled to help push the pram loaded with laundry for delivery. Boastfully Mickmac reported: 'They copped our Terence pinchin' from Mather's shop. Two tins o' salmon from off the counter. Dad gave him a beltin', O a real 'un, an' he's been sent to the Reformatory for six months.'

'It was his own fault,' Nobby said. 'You never see *me* whippin' two. One's enough. Get your hand under an old woman's shawl when she's leanin' agen the counter ... '

'And d'you know what,' Mickmac interrupted. 'Five lads from Bury Street came and offered to fight Bert Harrington — one down t'other come on. You should've seen it. Five of 'em, all lined up in front of Bert on the croft.' He struck a pugilistic attitude and began to throw punches. 'He went through the five of 'em like a dose o' salts. Didn't he, Nobby?'

Nobby was not listening. He was looking with envy at our shop. He said, mournfully: 'I wish we were rich and had a shop. Come on, Mick, my mam's waiting for the money.'

So were my parents. With the exception of three, the faithful among the patrons from the old shop gradually fell away as regular customers, though one or two still paid an occasional Sunday-morning visit. Two who remained staunch were Dick Dacre the blacksmith-farrier, and young Bert Harrington who was sweet on Dick's daughter Katie. They were Sunday-morning customers arriving in style in Dick's smart dog-cart drawn by the apple of his eye, a mettlesome high-stepping and prize-winning hackney called Billy Lad. They fed Dad's hungry ears with the week's store of news from the old quarter. The other customer who could be depended upon was Grandfather. He, too, had problems. His highly skilled craft, that of building coaches, carriages, phaetons and broughams, had seen its best days. He had a few years to go before becoming eligible, at seventy, to draw the joint ten shillings a week old-age pension for himself and

Grandmother. His latest news was the rumour that the company were to institute an age limit of sixty-five and, were he turned off, other masters, despite the high quality of his work, would not be likely to put a man of his advanced years on their payroll. Moreover, the long years he had given to socialistic and trade union activities did not endear him to employers.

'You are not to worry about it, Father,' Mother said flatly.

'Listen to her,' my father said, irritably. 'Dammit, woman. What d'you expect him to do?'

'He has seven married children, Tom Greenwood, and it would be coming to something if they couldn't scratch up two shillings a week each.' Grandfather was making murmurs of protest but Mother would not be silenced. Indignation shone in her eyes. 'I know what's bothering you, Father. But let me tell you *this*, nobody in our family is going to see the inside of the workhouse. *I* will see to that.'

'You've all got enough worries of your own, lass,' he said.

On this undeniable truth my father expressed himself forcibly when, as the days went by, local trade remained negligible. The appeal of Dad's genial familiarity and his robust brand of humour was out of place in this genteel neighbourhood.

'My *Christ*,' he protested, 'what's the matter with 'em all?'

Mother tried to reassure him. 'You can't expect to build a business in five minutes.'

'Five minutes? Ten blasted weeks and more we've been here. How much longer is the landlord going to wait for the rent? And what about the County Court threat for the fixtures and fittings?'

'Setbacks come to everybody,' she said. 'Whatever we owe will be paid off, have no fear of that. And while you've got time on your hands you should take advantage of it. Off into the park with you and get some fresh air into those lungs of yours.'

Coming home unsuspectingly from school one day I was stopped in the act of entering the kitchen by the sight of two silent men, utter strangers, sitting at our table, not by invitation but by process of the law. The upshot was our return to the old district, minus most of our worldly goods. Whatever my mother felt about it she kept to herself.

# 6

# *As You Were – and a Prophecy*

When we returned to another shop in the old district the warmth of the reception accorded to Dad by his old customers filled him with animation.

All knew of our misfortune but, as everybody perpetually stood in danger of a similar visitation, if this had not already happened, it was taken as a matter of course. Mother's determination to pay off what was owed did not meet with everybody's approval; indeed, some were emphatic that she ought to have circumvented the law with the time-honoured custom of 'doing a moonlight'.

She made the acquaintance of a Miss Bland, proprietress of a confectionery shop on the next corner. This had a de-served reputation for a wide delicious variety of eatables all of which Miss Bland and her staff prepared and cooked on the premises. Mother discovered that she had things in common with Miss Bland, who was a large lady given to wearing heavy Victorian gold bangles, brooches, cameos and gold chains that hung round her neck in many loops. First, Miss Bland was a native of north Staffordshire, close by my mother's birthplace; secondly, the living accommodation above Miss Bland's shop was crowded with damask-covered chairs and other handsome furniture, and hung with silk-velvet curtains. She also possessed sets of exquisite lace doilies and napery of the most expensive quality, all these treasures having been picked up at auction sales in the homes of rich mill-owners and 'carriage folk' who either had died or, following the footsteps of fashion, had removed to the pleasances of the Cheshire countryside.

My father listened to her raptures on Miss Bland's

possessions but, when she told him that she had accepted a
general cleaner's job offered by Miss Bland, he stared at her
affronted. 'Charring?' he said, as though unable to believe
it. '*You?*' He went on, indignantly, 'I never thought *I'd* live
to see the day when *my* wife descended to that.'

'Your wife is going to see that what we owe is paid off,'
she answered, continuing quickly when she saw his changed
expression, 'I know. I know. The debts aren't your fault.
But they're there and they're to be paid off, nolens volens.'

This was not the first job that she had been offered. The
other had come from Mr Wheelam who was 'overlooker' at
one of the biggest of the weaving sheds where mother had
worked for a time before her marriage. Each 'piece' that
came off the looms also came under his microscopic inspection. One end of it was thrown over a head-high roller placed
against the light while Mr Wheelam stood, as in a tent,
pulling the piece down yard by yard on the look-out for
defects in weaving. Each one detected meant a money fine
against the weaver with no allowance made for poor warp
or weft over which the weaver hadn't any control.

Rotund, flat-footed, unmarried, he resided with his plump
sister who, too, was single. A heavy gold chain gleamed
across his bulging middle; there was a big gold watch in the
right-hand pocket of his waistcoat and, in the left-hand
pocket on the chain's other end, a silver box specially designed to receive sovereigns and half sovereigns. These were
stored in spring-loaded cylindrical compartments with a slit,
like that of a money box, at the top of each. Through these
the coins could be thumbed as required. When in conversation he was fond of fiddling with this absent-mindedly.

He was on his doorstep, his sister standing behind him,
when, as Mother passed with me tailing, he made her the
offer of a job in the weaving sheds. Both goggled when she
said: 'I have seen all that I wish to see of weaving sheds,' and
she added, 'Eight and sixpence after your fines, that's all I've

brought home many a time for a full week's work. No thank
you, Mr Wheelam. I would rather pick oakum.' She sailed
off majestically. I stood there looking at Mr Wheelam who
turned to regard his open-mouthed and equally affronted
sister. 'Well! That's after offering to put her on four looms.
Some people ought to be glad of anything.'

'In no position to pick and choose,' Miss Wheelam said,
huffily. 'No position at all — her with an ailing husband and
just had the bums in.'

Mr Wheelam's scandalized glance fell upon me. 'And look
at him,' he said, sizing up my skinny physique. 'Just look at
him.' His sister obliged. 'He'll never live, that lad.' He shook
his head and took a long, slow intake of breath through lips
pursed as though he were about to whistle. 'No, *he'll* never
live. Written all over him.' They retired within, jabbering
peevishly. Luckily, the paralytic fear which had hold of me
was banished by the deep voice of Mrs Boarder who asked:
'Is your mother at home, lad?'

I went with her into our kitchen. 'I thought I'd just pop
round, lass. Here,' she placed a small piece of coal, a lump of
sugar and a halfpenny on our table. 'These are for luck, lass.
Tom Greenwood's done my husband and our Harry many a
good turn cutting their hair for nowt when things've been on
the rough side. We don't forget, and we hope your luck
changes.'

'That's very kind of you, Annie ... '

'When I heard you were comin' here I got the key and
took a good sniff around, upstairs and down. I was going to
come round and let you know if there'd been any.'

'What?'

'Why, bugs o' course. I've only got to walk in any house,
'specially if it's empty, take a sniff or two and I can tell you
there and then if it's bug-ridden. Oh, aye. I'm always being
asked, you know. Another thing, lass, though I hope you
don't think I'm interfering. It's just — well, things bein' as

they are wi' you—but if you want anythin' pawning just let
me know. Some people don't like to be seen going in. I do a
lot of it for the neighbours and I watch that pawnbroker like
an hawk. Aye, but I hope you can keep out of his clutches.'

'So do I, Annie.'

'By gum, yes,' Mrs Boarder went on. 'Hope. You need a
hell of a lot of that when your husband works on the docks.
Work, did I say? Hanging around outside the dock gates they
are, hour after hour, and when there's a job called they're
like animals fighting among themselves to get in half a day's
work. Listen to me, though. This'll never do.'

'You're right there, Annie,' Mother agreed, animatedly.
'It never *will* do. You've heard what my father's always been
preaching: until working men get together there won't be
any change.'

'And that *is* a fact,' Mrs Boarder said, emphatically. 'My
feller and our Harry they both pay into the union and I'm
all for 'em going on strike though, begod, I live in dread
against the day they do. It sticks in my craw when the
bedding's got to go in pawn to get a bite to eat.' She forced a
smile. 'Oh well, we're still living.'

'Yes,' Mother said, optimistically, 'and spring is on the
wing. That's something to be thankful for.'

Laughter sounded from the shop. 'Listen,' Mrs Boarder
said. 'I'm glad yonder lad o' yours is back. Always sure of a
laugh when he's around.'

# 7
# *Another Prophecy*

Springtime and, with the warmer days, another stench added to the already tainted air, the expanding effluvium of countless privies in this place where main drainage was unknown.

Once a week towards the midnight hour Corporation workmen withdrew the fetid tin receptacles from a flap-door in the backyard wall and emptied them into an open horse-drawn box-cart pulled up in the street at the back entries' foot. Occasionally unsuspecting visitors to the privy could be surprised by boys and youths in search of revenge. Waiting at the known habitual time that the victim was in the habit of answering Nature's daily call the revengeful stood at the flap-door in the back entry listening in silence. They were armed with a slat from an orange box at whose end stood a candle stump fixed in its own grease. They waited until the victim made himself or herself comfortable and was lost in the study of the evening newspaper, then, quietly, raised the flap-door, took a sighting, applied the burning candle to the naked target and, on the ensuing howl of agony, disappeared.

'Who did it?' Mr Wheelam, outraged, presented himself in our shop doorway. His manner was apoplectic; he stood with his legs wide apart.

'What's up wi' thee now?' Dad asked, and he and the customers waited for the explanation which, when forthcoming, made everybody laugh. 'Now, that's what I really call arson,' Dad said, which seemed to upset Mr Wheelam even more.

'I'll find out who did it,' Mr Wheelam declared angrily. 'Nobody's goin' to set my arse afire. I'll get the police.'

'It's the fire brigade you want, lad,' Dad said and Mr Wheelam spluttered and stumped away like a man who had both legs in splints.

Bert Harrington then said, 'And that'll teach the sod to throw a bucket o' scalding water over my dog. Can he help it if Wheelam's bitch is on heat?'

Next to each privy was a dark noisome compartment for the reception of cinders and table refuse. It was called 'the midden' and was sometimes used by boys as places of concealment in games of hide-and-seek. Within, soon after the vernal equinox, the ubiquitous bluebottle and house-fly spawned pyramids of writhing maggots which competed with rats for decaying food.

Spring, the time for the annual clean-up assault by fathers and dutiful grown-up sons. The prescription was time-honoured and invariable: three-pennyworth of thirsty quicklime put into the tin bath, buckets of water thrown on it so that it boiled, bounced and rattled, then, when it had settled, a bag of blue stirred in. All hands on deck with brushes in stinking 'petties' and fetid middens and on faded backyard walls, both inside and out, until all were dazzlingly transformed by thick coats of sweet-smelling whitewash.

Now, in the quiet of the night when the moon was at the full, a fragile and heart-lifting beauty haunted the back entries. The custom persisted even after modern hygiene banished the tin privies, replacing these with what was called 'the W.C.', a thing of wonderment to juvenile minds. Marvellous! A box full of water which refilled itself no matter how many times the chain was pulled, nor did it ever spill over. The novelty quickly palled.

Springtime, when small boys put away their whips and tops and, with halfpenny fishing nets and glass jam-jars, risked a hearty whack across the backside from a park-keeper's stick while lost, at the duck pond, in the absorbing hunt for sticklebacks brilliant with love's gorgeous and

transient livery ... April, and along the Old Road to Eccles
where the 'carriage folk' lived, the soot-caked clumps of
rhododendrons hanging over the boundary walls of their
mansions erupted in splendid bursts of colour, vermilion,
pink and white. Above, the reaching arms of beech, elm,
birch and ash joined hands across the road in a rustling arch
of virgin green. Within days the glory was no more. Unseen
upon the fresh, sea-borne and waltzing winds, by night and
day, there hung the dark stain of the town's squalid breath to
mock and ravish the garland of the year.

This was our time, we who were young. Not a street, however mean, that did not have its group of little girls preparing
for the first of May. Each street, when that day dawned, had
its maypole, a broom handle festooned with coloured tissues
and hanging with multi-coloured ribbons. A ring of girls,
each holding a ribbon, in attendance on a diminutive May
Queen veiled with a piece of old lace curtain and carrying a
basket of posies and a collecting tin for the hoped-for
halfpenny contributions. Songs and dances at every door:

> We come to greet you here today
> And we hope you will not turn us away,
> For we dance and sing our merry lay
> Round the maypole ring ...

Carters, a fortnight before the great day, tying bulging
sacks to the nearside front wheels of their carts. We all knew
what was in them: sand, newspaper and the chains and steel-
work that went with the harness of their charges. There it
would lie tumbling, with each turn of the wheel, all the miles
the dray had to traverse, reappearing, glittering silver, on
the first of May in dazzling contrast with the sheen of the
horses' summer coats. Manes and tails plaited with straw and
intermingled with ribbons in yellow, green, blue and red;
single, double and sometimes triple tiers of brass bells,
'chimes', nodding and tinkling delightfully on headcollars.

Every draught animal gay with coloured decorations and brilliant accoutrements down to the humblest moke whose hard-up owner could afford no more than a pennorth of ribbon to tie on its forelock. All a gay May-morning tribute by shabby industrial streets to the ghost of Merrie England.

A month or six weeks from now and it would be somebody else's turn, the married women's, the one holiday of the year which those who could afford it could call their very own. It was organized by Mrs Boarder in whose window a card was exhibited lettered, without fee, by a local signwriter. This said:

Book Now.
MRS BOARDER'S PICNIC
to
THE SARACEN'S HEAD
Roast Duck, Green Peas & New Potatoes.
FIVE SHILLINGS
Weekly Payments Taken.

Mrs Boarder's book of account was opened soon after Christmas for the convenience of those ladies who, of necessity, could contribute no more than threepence or sixpence weekly for the excursion which lived and died on one summer's day, though the exciting anticipation and succeeding weeks' of happy reminiscence magnified its benison and poured its balm on many a weary mind and heart.

Dresses to be made, borrowed or re-furbished; fervent prayers offered for fine weather and, on the day of the picnic, the whole street a mass of bubbling movement long before the appointed time. Not a front door closed; everywhere Liberty Hall; a chattering procession of flushed women in and out of each others' houses for stays to be laced and tightened, dresses to button and millinery's feathers to be arranged.

Shouts from the older kids and a mad rush as the thirty-seater, two-horse wagonette hove in view. While still in

motion it was filled with a scramble of kids pushing, shoving,
squealing and piling on to the seats for the briefest of rides
until the wheels rolled to a stop outside Mrs Boarder's door.

Mrs Boarder, feathered and fussing, started the round-up.
Out the ladies came, smiling and laughing, their husbands
grinning from the doorstep and, by now, kids by the hundred
from adjoining streets. Tall ladies, short ladies, thin and fat,
some of the latter having to be pulled and pushed up the
wagonette steps.

In the roadway the photographer who, hired weeks ago,
had set up his camera and was irritably trying to shift the
ubiquitous kids out of camera range while waiting for
stragglers to take their places. Finally all were aboard, all
sitting rigidly, arms folded, looking over the heads of the
juvenile multitude. 'Keep perfectly still.' Dead silence. A
click of the shutter. 'Thank you,' and everything came to life
again. Tomorrow, postcard reproductions with 'Mrs
Boarder's Picnic' printed on the picture's lower half would be
exhibited for sale in the newsagent's shop window.

Almost invariably as the driver took up the reins there
would be an urgent signal from a passenger: 'Wait. Hold on
a minute,' and one of the ladies alighted and rushed into her
house to the general cry of 'Why didn't she go before she
got on?'

'It's the excitement. It always takes her that way.'

A round of applause when the relieved lady got back into
her seat. A crack of the whip and the wheels began to roll.
Dogs barking, husbands shouting and waving and some of the
kids, eyes streaming and faces contorted, bawling: 'I want to
go with you, Mam.'

'We won't be long, love; we're only going round the
corner.' All was drowned in the general hubbub as the
wagonette rattled away. Late that night at a time of which
none could be certain, the tired and happy wanderers returned, all singing, not all wearing their hats and not a few

unsteady on their legs, having to be helped down and assisted home by understanding husbands.

But all that was weeks ahead. This evening just before the first of May there was the sound of horses outside our shop. 'Whoa, there, lad.' I knew that voice: Bert Harrington's in whose shadow I and all my companions were proud to walk because he wasn't afraid of anything or anybody. He had worked with his father at the coal face until the old man was killed by a roof fall. 'Well,' Bert said after the funeral, 'the hole got me dad but it's not having me,' and he changed his job. There he was, standing on his lorry reining in his splendid charge Caesar, a huge black shire horse with four white socks. Dad followed me to the shop step where Mrs Boarder paused in passing. Before Bert had time to jump down there was another clatter of hooves, Dick Dacre and the incomparable Billy Lad high-stepping it like the champion he was. The youth sitting alongside Dick was his son Charlie, of Bert's age. They stopped.

Dad was at the kerb patting Caesar's neck when Mother came out with a carrot for each horse. Billy Lad got his first while Caesar raised his head, pricked his ears expectantly, his velvet nostrils fluttering as he made a noise sounding like 'Houyhnhnm' to which Mother answered as she gave him the carrot: 'All right. All right. You hadn't been forgotten.'

'Aye,' Mrs Boarder said, 'and it's about time his driver paid this shop a visit. Look at him up there. Starve the barber. That hair o' yours looks like straws in a muck-cart, Bert Harrington.'

'Better late than never, love,' Bert said, grinning. He jumped from the cart and went into the shop with Dick and Charlie, Mother and Mrs Boarder standing chatting while petting the horses. I stood on the shop step watching the horses and listening to the conversation within.

'Let Tom do my-lad-o here first, will you, Bert?' Dick said, sitting down. 'He's got to get along to his technical school.'

Instead of following his father's ancient trade Charlie was a votary of engineering to the point of infatuation. He was in the fourth year of his apprenticeship with a small engineering firm in Manchester whose principal, Mr Henry Royce, had, some years before, bought a French motor car. The performance of this had offended his fastidious sense of the right and proper. In consequence he had decided to make three new ones to his own design. It was to the development of this branch of the firm's trade that Charlie was utterly dedicated. Although he was genial, likable and had all else to commend him he was not my man. He smelled of oil, not provender, and perpetually his talk was of induction, compression, ignition and exhaust and, of course, his idol of idols, 'Pa Royce'. Between father and son existed a perpetual conflict of irreconcilables—horse versus machine.

'Well, Charlie,' Father said, snipping away, 'and how's the motor business?'

'Motor cars!' Dick Dacre said.

Charlie grinned at him through the mirror. 'He's off. You won't be told, will you, Dad. This is 1910. Blooming horses. I tell you ... '

'We know,' his father scoffed. 'Old Moore's Almanac, one penny. We've read all about it in there.

> Carriages without horses shall go
> And accidents fill the world with woe;
> And the world unto an end shall come
> In nineteen hundred and twenty-one.

Blather. Old women's tales.'

'Have it your own way, Dad,' Charlie answered imperturbably. 'Just tell me ... where're all your horse trams? Electric's taken over. What about Graham White? Flew over Buile Hill Park in his aeroplane. Look at the nobs on the Old Road. Cars, that's what they're going in for. Coachmen having to learn to be chauffeurs if they want to keep their jobs.' Bert Harrington shifted restlessly, got up, took off his jacket and, sitting down again, rolled up his shirtsleeves as Charlie concluded. 'Tell you, Dad, ten years from now you won't see a horse on the road.' Bert was sitting there in silence, staring at the lino, arms tightly folded, fists clenched.

'What d'you make of him, Tom?' Dick Dacre asked, despairingly.

'I dunno,' Dad said. 'They're noisy, stinking things, always breaking down.'

'You've never heard o' the ones we make breaking down. Silver Ghost, London to Edinburgh and back in top gear all the way. What about that?'

His father snorted: 'Too fast and too far.'

Charlie frowned as he looked at his father's reflection: 'I can't understand you all. Here's a machine, ten times stronger than any horse. It's there when you want it any time o' day and night, never gets tired, and when you've done with it, well, leave it there, forget about it. Finished.'

'My Christ!' his father exclaimed. 'Doesn't that just about sum it all up. Don't you understand? A horse isn't a machine. It's alive and breathing, flesh and blood, summat a man feels for, not summat you just leave there and forget about.'

'That's just it,' Charlie insisted. 'Don't you see? No Sunday work, no seven days a week feeding and mucking out. Aye, and there's the other thing: I've seen some of the carters leatherin' in with the whip when their lorries're overloaded.'

'Oh, yes?' Bert said. 'An' if ever I saw one doing that he'd know about it—and quick.' He put out his legs and crossed them. He was looking at his boots; a little smile parted his lips while a note of fond reminiscence crept into his voice. 'Tell you summat, Charlie,' he said and did not raise his eyes. 'Did a double journey last week, Caesar and me. Bolton and back, full load both ways. I nodded off in the cart coming back through Irlams o' th' Height and only wakened when the cart stopped.' He glanced at Charlie.

'And where were we? Back home. Would those motor cars o' yours do that?' Dick Dacre laughed and gave Bert a hefty nudge. Bert continued: 'As for Sunday work, that's no trouble to me. What's more, if my horse went sick I'd sit up all night with him like any other feller in the game that's worth his salt.'

'Course you would, Bert,' Charlie said. 'But I'm not talking about that. You wait. You'll see, before you know where you are you'll be driving a motor and horses'll be going for ten a penny.'

'*That* you'll never make me believe,' Bert said, flatly. 'Ten a penny? Caesar out there's worth—well, I wouldn't like to put a price on him. And there's a hundred and eighty horses in our stables alone. Get on with you, man. The company couldn't afford it.'

'Have it your own way,' Charlie said, airily. 'You'll see.'

'Will he, now?' his father said. 'Well, Mr Clever-clogs, you listen to me. There's another horse out there in the street and I'll tell you this ... All the golden sovereigns in this kingdom couldn't buy Billy Lad from me—and bedamned to all your motor cars.'

Charlie laughed and got up. 'Pay for my hair-cut, Dad, will you?' He looked at his watch. 'Coo! Look at the time—'

'Aye,' his father said, roughly. 'Off to the brain factory with you afore I lose my temper.'

Charlie laughed again and went off, whistling. His cock-sure attitude disturbed me. It aroused deep instincts that were appalled at the possibility of his prophecy coming to pass. The smell of oil banishing the scent of provender? Unthinkable.

When Dad had finished his work he, Bert and Dick stood on the step admiring Billy Lad and Caesar. 'Ay,' Dad said, on a deploring murmur. 'Geldings, the pair of 'em. What a damned shame.'

Softly, Dick called: 'Billy Lad.' Billy pricked his ears,

turned his head and his nostrils fluttered in a subdued whinny. Dick laughed, went across and made much of him, saying: 'And who's going to be all dolled up for the first of May and have his photo took?'

I pleaded to be given a ride and good old Bert swung my feather-weight on to a cushion of folded sacks. He jumped aboard and, reins in hand, called out, 'Get on, there, owd 'un,' and the great black horse broke into a bouncing trot as he made for home and the manger.

The Company's stables formed a double-storied quad-rangle, the heavy horses below, the light mounting broad, peat-strewn ramps to their quarters above. The big, enclosed cobbled yard served as park for drays and carts. I stood inside the stable's doorway when Bert led Caesar to his place. A long double row of stalls to my right and left with a broad aisle between, in each a horseman working overtime for love and not money, grooming his charge and making its coat resplendent for the first day of May. Over all hung the sweet perfume of hay and, in my ears, the pleasing sound of the horses' rhythmic munchings. It soothed and comforted, made Charlie Dacre's prophecy both extravagant and ridiculous.

When I turned to go I found myself looking at the ranks of drays and lorries, their shafts reared skywards like arms upraised in attitudes of surrender.

# 8

# *Trouble in the Camp*

---

'Strike', 'Lock-out'. The words commanded the headlines. Why the golden sovereign's purchasing power should have fallen to sixteen shillings, ordinary men did not know. All they knew, in terms the simplest of them could understand, was that it meant a wage cut of four shillings in the pound — and how many of them were lucky enough to be bringing home a pound a week?

Strike. Lock-out. Workers and employers in basic conflict. In place of the blaring dissonance of factory hooters and the cavalry clatter of clogs at dawn there was an eerie silence. Every day became like Sunday. Miners with their whippets squatting, working fashion, on their heels under our shop window; dockers on the street corner or sitting with engineers, textile workers and carters in the forum of our shop arguing the whys and wherefores and getting their shaves and haircuts gratis while the struggle went on.

'There you are, lass,' Dad said glumly when he gave Mother the week's meagre takings. 'Three jumps at the cupboard door, that'll be our dinner from now on, I suppose.'

'Everybody's in the same boat and we've lived on clean teeth before,' she answered, adding, as she removed the sugar basin when Dad was about to reach for a second spoonful, 'One is sufficient. Remember, there's another day, Tom Greenwood.'

The drastic effect on domestic exchequers geared to a hand-to-mouth economy was immediate.

'Rent?' Mrs Boarder's scoffing laugh resounded through the street. She paused by our shop. There was a pair of men's boots tied by the laces hanging round her neck and, under her shawl, a bulging burden was concealed. She stared at the rent-collector: 'Have you gone daft? When we see the colour o' wages agen you'll get the rent and not before. Out o' my way.' She elbowed him aside and went into our shop where Harry, her son, recognizing his Sunday boots and guessing their destination, protested: 'Hey, Ma ... '

'Shurrup,' she interrupted. 'You want to eat this week-end, don't you? Then say no more. You can do your Sunday courting in your clogs like many and many a more'll have to do. Though it'd look better if you and Bert Harrington went off with those ferrets of his and brought a few rabbits back. Unless you'd like us to start making pies of those racing pigeons o' yours.' She sailed majestically into our kitchen announcing herself with: 'It's only me, lass. Anything you want pawned?'

'No thank you, Annie.' Mother dropped her voice and became conspiratorial: 'I've managed to land a full-time job. Waitress. That high-class café in Manchester where all the cotton men go.' She winked. 'I haven't told his lordship yet. I was coming round to see you or Polly anyway. Will you see that Tom and the kids get their dinners? You know him.'

'O' course I will.'

'It's a godsend, that job. *I* don't know how we'd have managed with all this trouble.'

'You'd have had to do like the rest of us,' Mrs Boarder said and displayed her concealed burden. ' "Uncle's". His and our Harry's Sunday suits. And if the strike's still on next week it'll be the bedclothes, then my flamin' weddin' ring. And don't ask me what I'm going to do after that.'

For us who were young the air was charged with tension. Pickets at dock gates, pit heads and factories. Mass meetings where the men roared responses to union spokesmen's angry rebuttals of employers' and newspapers' denunciation of the strikers and their 'socialism'.

We, at school, came in for a warning lecture by the head-master against the nonsensical absurdity of this dangerous and revolutionary doctrine. Of all the teachers he was our favourite. He told stories; he made his lessons interesting. At the height of the conflict he mounted our teacher's desk, and in jocund manner explained: ' ... and these Socialists say that the nation's wealth should be divided equally. Well, do you know what each person in the British Isles would get if all the money *were* shared equally?' His smile broadened, his merry eyes roved the room. 'One pound, seventeen shillings and sixpence three-farthings.' He leaned back, beaming, waiting for the derisive burst of sycophantic laughter which we dutifully supplied.

'I don't like it, you know, Annie,' Dad complained when Mrs Boarder came bustling into our kitchen and took a pie out of the oven.

'There,' she said, ignoring Dad's remark. 'You've got Bert Harrington and our Harry to thank for that—not forgetting Bert's ferrets and somebody's rabbits.' She placed the pie in the table's centre. 'Get it while it's hot. And what is it you don't like now?'

'It's the missis—going out to work. I tell you, I don't like it.'

'*You* don't like it! There's thousands and thousands o' married women round here don't like it either but they're doing it. And if you don't like it there's only one thing you can do, lad: lump it.' She half turned. Nobby was standing in the doorway, his eyes longingly on the pie. 'And what's up wi' thee?' she asked.

'I've got bogies,' he said. 'The school nurse said I've ... '

'Come here. Let's be havin' a look.' She examined his tangled hair and made a wry face: 'Crawlin' alive.'

Nobby looked at Father: 'Me mamma said she'll pay you when me dad goes back to work.' He looked at the pie again, licked his lips and swallowed.

'Sit down. Sit down and get your dinner.' Mrs Boarder waved her hand as Dad was in the act of rising. '*I'll* do him.' She took a sheet of newspaper and tucked it into the neck of Nobby's jersey so that it had a distant resemblance to a seventeenth-century ruff. 'Let's see. Size double nought, isn't it, Tom?' She came back from the shop with the clippers. In seconds Nobby's thatch and pests were crackling in the fire and he was dismissed bald and salivating.

'That's that,' she said, preparing to go. 'See that you wash up after you've done. Oh, nearly forgot, you've got a paying customer. Old Billy Hartley's kicked the bucket. Undertaker wants you to shave the old lad before they screw him down — er —' she contracted her brows: 'What do they pay you for that, lad?'

'A tanner — and glad of it. My Christ, lass, it's come to summat when you earn more out o' the dead than the livin'.'

'Stop your gruntin'. That tanner'll feed you like fightin' cocks.' She turned to see who had come into the shop. 'Another payin' customer. You're doing well.' She winked and whispered: 'Old Wheelam. Ta-ra.' She went into the shop where she said: 'He's havin' his dinner. Sit yourself down or come back in half an hour. You've time on your hands like everybody else.'

Mr Wheelam sat down with a loud grunt. 'And that's none o' my desirin', Annie Boarder. Back at work, that's where they all ought to be. There's orders on orders pilin' up at the mills.'

'Aye? Then they shoulda thought about that afore they locked everybody out.'

'Oh? And somebody else ought to do a bit o' thinkin' too. There's all that tick that'll have to be paid off.'

'That's the last thing that's botherin' me. Bad as Ma Flarty, you are, the miserable old scut. And I wouldn't be in her husband's shoes if she natters him into blacklegging. If he was half a man he'd land her one.'

'And what about the property owners?' Mr Wheelam's tone was a mixture of whining petulance and indignation. 'Where do they come in? Arrears, arrears, arrears.'

'Oho! That's where the shoe pinches, is it?'

He raised his voice. 'We're entitled to our rents, aren't we?'

Mrs Boarder raised hers. 'No more than men're entitled to a livin' wage. Do you think they go on strike for the fun of it? Everythin' we've got going in the pawnshop. Not a bite in the house for tomorrow and not a shovel o' coal in the backyard. God above, man, the way things're going we'll none of us have a pot to piss in nor a window to throw it through. What's more, if you or any of your kidney think I'm going to put rent before kids skrikeing for food then you're stark, ravin' doo-lally. Poh! No patience with you.'

Police forces from distant towns came to reinforce the strength at dock gates, railway termini and other places where the nervous authorities were apprehensive of trouble. They were received with jeers and taunts, but the strikers' resentment of this was as nothing to their anger when the news went round of the arrival of the Scots Greys to garrison Salford. Then, abruptly, settlement and a return to work except for those whose conspicuous political and trades union activities made them marked men. Mrs Boarder's husband and others like him became invisible to the eyes of foremen when hands were being chosen for the gangs. Luckily for him he was strong and in his prime. This landed him a porter's job at Manchester's vast Smithfield Market.

There were others less fortunate. My mother's youngest sister burst into our kitchen flushed and furious.

'Do you know what's happened?' she demanded and answered her own question before Mother had chance to say a word. 'They've sacked Dad. There!'

Father swore. Aunt continued: 'Any excuse, that's what they've been waiting for all this time. *This* is where his politics and trades union's landed him.'

'You are talking like your husband.'

'Well, this has proved him right, hasn't it?'

'It has not. If the men *are* beaten now the fight will still go on, and never you forget that.'

'Augh! You and that Keir Hardie. Bad as my father. Always was and always will be.'

'Thank you for the compliment.'

'Well, how's Dad going to manage now? Who'll give him a job at his time of life? Go on. Tell me.'

'He has sons and daughters,' Mother reminded her. 'We shall all have to help the best we can.'

'What about his union and all the time and money he's given to that Labour Party? I suppose', she went on sourly, 'we'll hear no more from either of them.'

Frostily, Mother answered: 'What he's done in those quarters he did for what he believed in and not for anything he hoped to get out of it.'

The man who came to wear Grandfather's clothes was a stranger from him I had known. Within a month the old man had grown a silver beard: his vigorous activity ebbed and he sat in his armchair staring and silent.

# 9

# *Mother knows Best*

After the general return to work Mother ignored Dad's grumbling complaints and insisted on keeping her new job. 'My wages will help to pay off our debts,' she said, firmly. 'As for the tips—well, never mind about them.' She banked these at the local co-op for a purpose she declined to disclose. Gifts of unwanted food from the café's chef were brought home daily in her capacious shopping bag and these augmented our diet and that of my grandparents and any neighbour whose need was known to be desperate.

My mother, furthermore, now decided that my education at the council school was wanting in a most important particular—music. She had made a move already to correct this. Playbills from the local theatres were displayed in our shop and, for this service, Father was given complimentary tickets. Those to do with the music hall were his preserve; drama in any form and, above all, opera, grand or comic, was Mother's. The record of her attendance of these over many years was kept in a cupboard drawer in the form of programmes jealously preserved.

Already she had had a brush with my headmaster who, meeting Mother and me in the theatre foyer as we came out after a performance of *Faust*, paused, stopped and said: 'Do you think *Faust* suitable for a boy of his years, Mrs Greenwood?'

Mother mounted her high horse, answering, 'Where the good things of this life are concerned you cannot begin too young.' As we walked away she said to me, huffily: 'Too young, indeed,' and her indignation was still on the simmer when we arrived home, but this evaporated as, after looking at the programme before adding it to the collection, she suddenly began to warble the 'Jewel Song'. Dad, recalling his wife's oft-repeated and well-intentioned criticism that his was an untrained voice, commented: 'From the sound of things somebody else could do with a few singing lessons.'

'That somebody doesn't happen to have been blessed with a voice like yours, Tom Greenwood, or the lessons would have been forthcoming, make no mistake about that.' She sighed yearningly. 'Oh, what would I give to be able to sing.' She turned on him: '*You* would have made a magnificent Mephistopheles, you devil, you.'

Dad kept a straight face and looked at the ceiling. 'Operatic heroes! Not a real man among the lot.'

She jumped to their defence instantly. 'What do you mean? They're more than real to me.'

'And I'd like to hear what tune you'd be singing if you had to live with one of 'em. You haven't their socks to darn and shirts to wash. It's roses all the way and ... '

'Of course,' Mother said, loftily, 'if that is your attitude the matter is closed.' Dad retired to the shop chuckling.

Having made up her mind on a course of action she did not waste time. She arrived from work one evening to find my sister and me in the shop listening to adult conversation. Without preliminary she said to Dad: 'Attend to his hair,' and she glanced indicatively at me.

Talk subsided among the customers and, when my father asked for explanation, a small cardboard box was produced from Mother's bulging bag. From this she took a brand-new Eton collar and a bow tie. 'There's a voice test at St Thomas's tonight,' she said. 'I want him to try for a place in the choir.' To my dismay she continued: 'Choir practice Tuesdays and Fridays and two services every Sunday. *That* will help to keep him off the streets *and* he'll learn something.'

'If he's anything like his father,' Dad said, 'it'll learn him to wish he was out of it. Ah, well,' he went on, and I detected the note of sympathy, 'I had it myself to do when I was his age.'

Mother looked at him incredulously: 'You! In the choir?'

'Of course I was,' Dad retorted, a little put out by his wife's unflattering astonishment. 'I never wanted to go but the parson hooked me in. St Paul's. He bought me a pair o' boots, too, because my clogs made a clatter in the aisle.' He grinned and looked at his customers. 'Aye, lads, many and many a bright shillin' those boots fetched for my mother at the pawnshop.' The men laughed, but when Dad saw Mother's frowning expression he said, '*Now* what's wrong?'

I did not share Mother's gratification on my admission to the choir of St Thomas's and I resented being dragged on a tour of her relatives and the fact paraded. While this was in process there were, ringing in my sullen and sulky mind, the doleful words ' ... choir practice Tuesdays and Fridays ... morning and evening service every Sunday ... That will keep him off the street.' The latter privation was something I bitterly resented and in my heart of hearts I wished Mother were more like Mrs Boarder or Mickmac's mother and all others who seemed not to mind their offspring enjoying, in their own fashion, the all-too-brief and frisky days of childhood.

I was not turned loose even when the tour ended and we were walking down our street. 'You can go out and play when we're home and that collar is off. *That* is for Sundays and choir practice.' We stopped outside Mrs Boarder's open front door. Polly Mytton was sitting on the chair by the dresser. 'Is Annie at home, Polly?'

'Come in, love,' Mrs Boarder bawled. 'Anything wrong?' she asked, when we entered.

'It's ... Parcel of food I've brought from the café, Annie. Send your Hetty round to the shop, will you. And you, Polly. Look in, will you, there's a bit for you. It's nice of you both to help with Tom and the children.'

'Go on with you, woman,' Mrs Boarder said. 'If a neighbour can't help a neighbour it's come to summat.'

Off-hand, Mother mentioned my admission to the choir.

'Now! Well! There!' Polly said, eyeing me admiringly: 'What a masher. And isn't he growing.' She laughed. 'Soon be starting work and bringing wages home. How old is he now?'

'Eleven in December.'

'Eleven! Already? How the years do fly.'

'They do that, begod,' Mrs Boarder said, and sighed. 'Well, I've had my fill bringing up a family — not that I've a complaint against any of 'em, but I want no more. There's Alice Radcliffe I've just left. Like a bear with a sore head 'cause there's another on the way. Bottle after bottle o' pennyroyal she's supped but it hasn't worked. My God! I thought things were bad enough for me, but her ... Eleven of 'em, and now another, and him only bringing home eighteen shillings a week when he can get it. If he was mine I'd've told him to blow on it long ago.'

Polly, slowly twisting her wedding ring round her finger, murmured: 'Oh well, that's the way it is. Some have too many and some ... I was never blessed but many's the time I wished I had been. Ay, I'd ha' loved childer about the house. God's will. It wasn't to be.'

Voices at the front door. Bert Harrington and Harry Boarder. 'Been out running, they have,' Mrs Boarder said. 'Thank God he's back in time; I was getting worried.' Harry came in and wished Mother and Polly a good evening as he put his spiked running pumps on the table's edge.

His mother said, ' — er — h'm', and scratched her cheek. 'I — er — I'm a bit short till pay day, lad.' She pointed to the running pumps. 'Let's have 'em for pawn, will you? I'll have 'em out again by Sat'day for certain.'

'Course, Mam. Help yourself,' he said and went into the backyard to commune with his racing pigeons.

'He never lets me down,' Mrs Boarder said to Mother. 'By the way, how's your dad?'

'What can you expect, Annie?'

Mrs Boarder shook her head. 'Never seen such a change come over a man so quick. That's what comes o' being honest. What a blooming life.'

'We're all helping as much as we can,' Mother said, rising.

'Aye, well, better be off. I've got to get a cough bottle for Tom. It's started to bother him again.'

'If I were you I'd get him a few bottles o' stout. He's losing a bit of weight, I notice. Aye, and while you're at it, sup one or two yourself. You're working too hard.'

'Nay,' Mother answered. 'Mustn't put temptation his way.'

Mrs Boarder laughed and slapped her thigh. 'You can put it my way any time you've a mind, love.' She, too, got up and reached for the running pumps. 'If I don't get these into Uncle's before they close there'll be nowt for their breakfasts in the morning. And I'm glad you've got the lad in the choir, lass. By gum, it's a long time since I saw the inside of a church. But I haven't forgotten the hymns.' She began to sing and Polly joined in:

'The King of love my Shepherd is
Whose goodness faileth never ... '

Mother took up the tune, humming softly, as we went home.

# 10

# Something to Think About

'Here,' my father said and gave me a shilling and a sixpence. 'Take it round to your grandmother's, don't lose it — and another thing, if I hear that you've taken as much as a crumb from her you'll get a taste of that.' He pointed to the leather strap which hung conspicuously from its nail at the side of the fireplace. 'Tell her we'll be calling on Wednesday after your mother gets home from work.' He walked to the sofa and lay down, leaving me with the weekly contribution which he and Mother made towards my grandparents' support.

Mickmac was outside the shop muttering to himself and tapping the pavement with a bare foot. 'Tee-you, kay-you. Tee-you, kay-you' he was saying, puzzlingly. I asked him what the game was. 'Double-tongueing practice,' he explained, baffling me still further. 'Where're you going?'

'To my grandma's with the money.'

'Come on, then.' He fell into step. 'Triple-tongueing,' he explained. 'You've got to say Tee-you-tee-you, kay-you-kay-you.'

'But what's it all for?'

He looked at me astonished. 'Why, when you want to play the cornet. Nobby's learned it me. He's joined the junior band. An' I'm putting my name down. You know what? If you learn to play real good they'll give you a job for life, a good 'un, like at Foden's. But he's going to try for Besses o' th' Barn — when he's learned, I mean. They go all round the world playin' and they pay your fare and give you wages. And you see this?' He dug into his pocket and produced a foolscap four-leaf folder whose cover read:

Pendleton Co-operative Industrial Society Ltd.
Quarterly Report and Balance Sheet.

'One and thrippence he earned with 'em last Sat'day night. I'm going to have a go. In a box, they are, on the wall in the head office. You just help yourself. Then you wait outside the pubs on a Sat'day night till the Salvation Army comes round with the band and the girls go in sellin' *War Cry* to the drunken men. *That's* when Nobby nips in wi' these. You should've seen him, just as though they were newspapers. There he was shoutin' out: "Special! Special! Reeeepo' 'n Balance Shee, one penny. He'y'are. Special! Reeeepo' 'n Balance Shee, one penny." One and thrippence, I tell you, an' he only gave his mother the odd thrippence. *I*'d've given mine the shillin'.' He changed the subject saying, yearningly, 'Wouldn' it be marvellous, being took on by Besses o' th' Barn Band and goin' all round the world! Ooo, heck.'

Grandfather was sitting in his chair, both hands on the stick he had taken to using. I put the money on the table and delivered Father's message. Mickmac, who had not accompanied me before, stood looking at Grandfather's glass-fronted bookcase until Grandma began to cut two slices of bread and margarine which she sprinkled with sugar. 'There you are, boys,' she said, in her quiet voice; 'and be very careful when you are crossing the road.'

What I liked about Grandma was her gentleness. She insisted on my cultivating 'good manners' which, she said, 'are at all times pleasing.'

On her bed was what now would be a museum piece, a coverlet decorated with biblical quotations in coloured cut-out letters and sewn with the fine stitchery becoming one who, as a girl, had been first sewing-maid to a Lady Waterpark.

'Coo!' Mickmac said awed, as we strolled home. 'All those books! Are they his?'

3

We bumped into Nobby. As usual he was burdened with the perambulator. 'Hey,' he said, staring at Mickmac. 'Your ma's bawlin' her head off for you to take your dad's dinner.' Mickmac scooted. Nobby looked at me, indignantly. 'She wanted *me* to tek it—for nothin'. Poo!' None of the four babies in the pram was of his kin. The resourceful boy explained that during these, the school holidays, he had organized a daily service delivering babies to their weaver mothers employed at one of the mills. 'Thrippence a week, *each*,' he said, adding, as though I were backward in arithmetic; 'that's a shillin' and me mam gives me a penny back.' One of the children started to howl; Nobby snarled at it: 'Yaa, shurrup, you mardy-arse,' then he said to me: 'Tell you what. I'll let you come with me if you want.' He opened his eyes wide. 'You should see the mill engine and all the machinery. Thousands and *thousands* o' wheels going round.' I swallowed the bait and, when we were on our way he said, bossily, 'Come on, then, come on. Push.'

Now and again a small boy passed us at the double. Each carried a basin with saucer as a lid and tied up in a red handkerchief with white spots. This was their father's or brother's hot midday meal.

We stopped at the mill lodge in whose window hung a card saying: HANDS WANTED. NO IRISH NEED APPLY. The lodge keeper looked through the small slide window and said: 'All right.'

The din of the looms could be heard yards distant but when Nobby pushed open the weaving shed's doors the racket was overwhelming. Looms in close-packed lines separated by narrow aisles, each loom adding its stuttering clamour to the horrid pandemonium that drowned even the whirr of overhead countershafting and the slow-flapping applause of drive belts. One woman to every four looms and, midway down the shed against the windows, corpulent Mr Wheelam at his work inspecting the finished pieces. Some of the women, I noticed, were talking to each other. Oh, yes. Lip reading. My mother had described to me this means of communication.

The babes in the pram were screeching though their howlings were inaudible. I saw Mr Wheelam take out his watch and stand with it in his hand as he looked upwards through the window at the mill buzzer conspicuous above the engine house. A white jet of vapour under pressure plumed forth and another shrill note was added to the general discord. Weavers threw the driving belts on to the idler pulleys; the deafening clatter stopped abruptly though its echoes still pounded my ears. A burst of chatter, a clattering of clogs as the weavers lined up with pint mugs at a gas geyser and brewed tea. The mothers claimed their screaming offspring, sat on the floor by the looms and began to suckle their infants while friends put steaming pints of tea at their sides and whatever it was had been brought to eat.

For me there was a hovering malevolence about the place. I could feel its stifling and crushing influence. Instinct, nervous and alert, urged me to be out and away, never to return. I did not wait for Nobby. I sidled out of the door and made for home.

As I turned the corner at the far end of our street Mickmac came rushing to me all eyes and urgency: 'Hey,' he said, his voice little more than a whisper, 'hey, your dad's dead.'

There was a crowd round the shop, mostly women; their conversation was subdued. 'Only forty-five, though.' 'My God! Whatever's she going to do?' Polly Mytton was weeping. Mrs Boarder collected my sister and me and took us to her house where she directed her dark-eyed daughter Hetty to look after us until further notice. She added, threateningly, to Hetty: ' ... and see that you do, think on, unless you want a good scutch across the ear-hole.'

As was the case with almost every other man in the

locality, my father left this world in the state in which he had entered it—penniless.

After the funeral we moved to another house near by and somebody introduced Mother to a gentleman whose honesty could be vouched for though he, too, hadn't any money. He took over father's business and promised to pay the agreed price by instalments. This arrangement he dishonoured, quietly disposing of everything portable for cash, then disappearing without trace.

'The rotten sod-pot!' Mrs Boarder said furiously. 'Doing it on a widow with childer.' She put out her muscular arms. 'Let me meet up with him anywhere and get these maulers on him. He'll be on his back and I'll bash his brains out, begod I will. What're you going to do, lass?' Her voice was full of concern. Mother shook her head.

'Look, lass,' Mrs Boarder said. 'Get round to the Board o' Guardians with the childer. They'll have to give you out-relief.'

'Nay, Annie. I couldn't plead poverty. It'd stick in my craw.'

'Don't you talk so daft, woman. That's just what they want you to do. How're you going to manage rent, grub and clothes for three on what you earn?'

Mother made murmurs expressive of uncertainty.

Mrs Boarder exclaimed irritably, 'I'd take money from the devil himself afore I'd go out to work and leave my childer running wild. I tell you, lass, if it'd been my husband I'd be there holding both hands out, my Christ I would.'

We went, Mother, Sister and I, to the Board. A row of wooden forms faced a table at which the three Guardians sat. There could not be any doubt as to what they were guarding. This was in a canvas bag on the table in front of them. There was an account book at its side.

The applicants were old men and women for the most part. They sat there dejected, motionless and silent except for wheezes and coughs. When the old men were called to the table for interrogation each took off his cap respectfully and stood holding it in front of him with both hands.

Our turn came. My sister and I stood either side of Mother facing the Guardians. The canvas bag was open in front of the paymaster, coins spilling from its mouth. Mother answered the questions; the Guardians put their heads together and mumbled, then the paymaster, looking at the applicant said: 'Very well. Half a crown.' He took a coin from the store and tossed it across the table. It bounced, revolved on its rim and stopped. The man reached for his pen to enter the item in the accounts.

Mother did a startling thing. She left the coin where it lay and electrified the room by announcing, in a ringing voice: 'Half a crown? Half a crown for three for a week?' I looked up at her alarmed. Her back was as straight as a guardsman's. She tossed her head, defiantly. 'I would not demean myself. I would sooner sing for our crusts in the gutter. Come along, children.' There was no comment from the Guardians nor a round of applause from the audience. As I turned to follow I saw the paymaster reach for the coin and slide it back into the hoard. 'Next,' he said, and a tiny old lady in clogs and shawl, bony hand clutching a shiny door key, came apprehensively to the table. She was followed by her husband stooping over a walking-stick.

# II

# A Leg Pull

Mother's troubles were partly eased by a joint household arrangement with my grandparents, the advantage for her being the knowledge that, while she was at work, Grandma was in the house to play mother. But instead of having two children to cope with, Grandma found that she had three. Soon after having been discarded, the shadows gathered round Grandfather's faculties. A chair-bound paralytic took the place of the vigorous man I had known. During Mother's absence at work Grandma managed him and us with uncomplaining patience, though she, too, was not the same.

But her hearth-rug tales for ever enthralled. Stories of a country childhood, of her father's garden, its fruit trees, the well and the deep, swift-running trout stream at the garden's foot glowed in a never-never land of perpetual summer. Nowadays though, when at our insistence she told us once again of those happy, far-off Arcadian days, her wavering voice would tail away and her chin sink on to her chest. Not long afterwards both she and Grandfather slipped away into the longest sleep of all.

Mother then charged me with the care of my sister. 'Look after her while I'm at work,' she said, 'and remember, wait for her after school and bring her home safely. I've arranged with Miss Bland. There's the two plates.' She pointed to the two plates on the table. 'Take them to her shop when you come home at dinner-time and she'll give you what I've ordered. I've left something for your teas in the cupboard. Mrs Boarder and Polly Mytton's going to keep their eyes on you.' There was a note of warning in the latter sentence. 'Be a good lad, now. Don't play with fire and keep out of mischief.'

We did not see her again until after seven o'clock. Of necessity she was obliged to profane the Sabbath by doing the weekly wash on that holy morning, but it was always hanging in our backyard by the time I returned from morning service, except, of course when it decorated the clothes-horse because of rain. In the afternoon while my sister and I were at Sunday School she baked bread. The evening saw her with Polly Mytton and my sister in the church gallery immediately opposite my place in the choir.

It was now that I earned my first money. This was a half-crown fee paid for my attendance at the one and only choral wedding during my term as chorister. When I handed the money to her she said: 'Right. This goes into the bank for your future.' I was given a penny. 'And remember this — when your voice has broken you aren't giving up music and don't you ever forget it, young man. Five pounds, that's what Miss Bland says a piano can be picked up for at the auction sales.' She pointed to a corner of the room. 'That's where it will go and instead of gadding around like a street Arab while I'm at work you'll be in front of it practising.' She concluded on a yearning sigh as she threw her glance upwards, 'What I would have given if I'd had a chance like that when I was your age.'

The money she earned at the restaurant being inadequate, she resumed casual employment with the firm of contracting caterers. Postcards arrived irregularly asking her to report at this or that town hall or assembly rooms to help serve a dinner or banquet. This meant that, immediately her work at the restaurant was finished, she had to rush to wherever the function had been arranged to help unpack all the crockery and cutlery, lay the tables, serve the food, then wash and pack everything afterwards, by which time the midnight hour had struck and all public transport stopped.

On these occasions our instructions were invariable: 'Now listen, children, both of you. No later than half past eight. Understand? Bed, the pair of you. You are not to have anybody in and if anybody knocks on the door ignore them.' She looked at me: 'Before you go to bed bolt the front and back doors top and bottom and don't forget to put the string out of the window. Oh, and the fire. You don't need to have one halfway up the chimney. Coal costs money, don't forget,' muttering to herself: 'Sixpence a hundredweight, indeed. They must think folks are made of money.'

The window string was, literally, a leg pull. Having had to walk home after the banquet and with doors bolted from the inside Mother, as the parish church clock struck half past one or two o'clock, reached for the string weighted with a chip of wood which hung from my bedroom window and gave it several tugs. The other end, tied to my ankle, did the needful and I came down to open the door. Laboriously she heaved 'the bag' on to the table and, removing her hat pins, said: 'Go on back to bed, laddie. I've just got to have five minutes before I face those stairs.' She flopped into her chair: 'Ay, deary me. I'm so tired.'

The injunction to be in bed by eight thirty was absurd. At that time street games were at their height though, around nine, the moment came when children with fathers and mothers were called in for bed. The few who were without parental supervision formed a freemasonry devoted to mutual entertainment which was indulged until long after bedtime. Needless to say this fellowship was exclusively male. Being handicapped by the responsibility of a pestering sister it was my habit to push her into the house, order her to bed and threaten her with a thumping if she disobeyed.

I was then away to our favourite haunt, the home of the Seeleys, newcomers to the locality, a family of three boys whose father was on night shift. Mr Seeley was said to be a widower but Mrs Flarty asserted that Mrs Seeley had 'run off' with another man. For this uncharitableness she had come in for a public ticking off from Mrs Boarder.

'You're at it agen, you back-bitin' old besom.'

'The truth's the truth, isn't it?'

'It's a long time since that was on your tongue. Another thing, I'd like to see the feller that'd want to run off wi' thee, you faggot. An' if you spent more time inside with that brush o' yours your house'd be a sight cleaner.'

Billy Seeley, the eldest of the boys, apart from being a competent performer on the accordion, had a consuming interest in matters pertaining to the preservation of health both human and animal, especially his own. His medical knowledge derived from a prized possession, a second-hand book entitled *Dr M'Tartle's Illustrated Household Physician & Veterinary Guide*. The study of this volume convinced Billy that he had symptoms of many ailments. Over these he was not in the least melancholy. Quite the contrary. On their mantelpiece was a miscellaneous collection of patent medicines in pill and liquid form, free samples he had applied for by filling in 'name and address in BLOCK LETTERS enclosing 1d. stamp'. With these he doctored himself and, free of charge, any boy or girl prepared to submit to his treatment.

Our other companion was Alfie, also a newcomer, a motherless lad older than us but who looked younger because of his lack of inches. Mickmac and I first found him against the wall in the shadows by the greengrocer's shop. He was catching his breath in stifled sobs.

Mickmac said: 'What's up, lad?' Alfie did not answer, he was too full of grief. We persisted until, finally, Alfie said: 'He hadn't any money for the beer so he killed it.'

'What?'

'Me rabbit. Hit it with the poker. There.' He looked at the carcase hanging outside the shop in the light of the spluttering naphtha flare. 'He says he's goin' to drown himself and tek me with him.'

'You come with us, lad,' Mickmac said. 'Here. I'll tell you what. I've got two mice: I'll gie you one. It won't cost you nothin' to feed. Bert Harrington'll allus gie you a handful of oats from the stables.'

Cowed and shrinking, Alfie's nervous, propitiatory smile invited your sympathy. His father stayed in the pubs until closing time or until his money ran out. If the cupboard were empty, as it all too often was, Alfie had to fend for himself. My sister and I shared our toast, dripping and tea with him betimes. He also found a fish-and-chip shop proprietor who had charity in her heart. When, around eleven o'clock, the lady was about to close the shop he came out of the shadows, went to the counter and asked: 'Are there any scratchings, mam?' Scratchings was our name for the tiny globules of fat that accumulated in the bottom of the fryer. She scooped these into a paper together with any other left-overs and passed them to Alfie, who stood outside wolfing them. His signal to be home and abed was when 'Sweet Adeline', in tipsy harmony, announced the imminent return of his belted parent. If he were caught Alfie dodged the clumsily swung belt and disappeared into the night and the refuge offered by Ted Grimshaw, who was night man at a local mill with the job of attending the boiler. He made Alfie a rough and ready bed of sacking in the firehole and Alfie enthralled us with his description of this enviable experience. 'It's lovely down there. All warm. The noise o' the fire roarin' away all the time. Sends you right off to sleep. And in the mornin' Ted gives me a big bowl o' water, all hot to wash me in, then he gives me a mug o' tea fresh-brewed and anythin' that's left over in his dinner basket for me breakfast.' He added, 'I'd rather have it there any time than Throstle Nest Mill.'

'Where's that?'

'Where we were afore we came here. The night watchman there used to let me sleep on the bales o' cotton when me dad was at me. Nice old man, he was, and I wasn't frightened of the quiet and the dark when I knew he was around with his dog and I could hear him practising.'

'Practising what?'

'Tin whistle. Practising, he said, for when they gave him the sack and then he could go around all the streets playing on it and earn pennies. But you give me Ted Grimshaw's firehole any time. Oh, it's lovely and warm down there.'

Billy Seeley got up, opened their oven door and stood back half a pace out of the way of the heat. 'That's how we warm our bed,' he said, pointing to the three bricks within. 'Wrap 'em in a bit of old blanket and it's a treato.'

'We don't have a fire except o' Sundays,' Alfie said. 'But when I get cold I wait until I hear him snorin' then I go downstairs and get our hearth-rug and put it over me in bed.'

'Never mind, Alfie, lad,' Billy said. 'Let's have a sing-song.' Out came his accordion and we sang all the current popular songs until the gas began to 'beg', that is, it began to flicker a warning that unless you were quick with another penny you would be sitting in the firelight glow. This was no hardship. The lateness of the hour, the silence of the streets and the kitchen's reaching shadows set the stage for Billy to tell his ghost stories of graveyards and of solitary travellers benighted and dogged by moaning wraiths over desolate heaths. Billy brought his alarming performance to its close when he judged that our fear was at its height. 'Come on. That's enough. Home, the lot o' you. Bedtime.'

I knew that my sister would be abed and asleep but between home and me stood the deserted streets and the challenge of our dark and silent kitchen. Beforehand, though, I had made arrangements to defeat the fiendish powers of night. I had put plenty of newspaper in the grate of my bedroom and two more sheets were rolled into long, loose cylinders and left handy under the sofa. A quick dash home, slam and bolt the door top and bottom, light the paper torches at the fire, then, with one forrard and one aft, hurry upstairs and set fire to the newspaper in the grate. When this blazed, shove the string through the window, undress, tie the string round my ankle, dive under the bed-clothes and gabble prayers. Safe. Comforting thoughts of Ted Grimshaw's boiler hole; soothing sounds of the great fire roaring in the fire box, a long and pleasing drone that faded on a diminuendo, then away and away on a slow delightful glide to sleep ... until the string was pulled.

# 12

# The Man of the House

The Declaration was electrifying. Patriotism's siren promises took command and men joyfully cast aside the dreary monotony of work in mill and factory to join the excited and eager crowds at the doors of recruiting offices.

Bert Harrington, Harry Boarder, Harry's father and others disappeared abruptly from the local scene and, when they were gone, wives and mothers said: 'Ay, I just can't get used to it, them not coming home o' night.'

There were other changes. Gold half-sovereigns in wages might now be replaced by the novelty of a ten-shilling note which was paraded excitedly before friends who, to be in the swim, went out of their way to exchange their gold for the pieces of paper.

For us lads who had the greatest affection for him the most arresting item of war news concerned Dick Dacre, whose smithy and the music of its anvil was a source of perpetual pleasure. What we heard was of no pleasure to anybody. With other horses of the district the army authorities had commandeered the nonpareil, the matchless Billy Lad, even though ' ... all the golden sovereigns in the kingdom wouldn't take Billy Lad from me ... '

Those unforgettable words had been retailed by me to all my companions and now, here we were on the fateful day, a subdued group of boys hanging round the smithy door waiting for the dreadful moment. The place was devoid of its customary cheerfulness. Tom Broadbent, who had a bald head, a big belly and a broad leather belt whose enormous brass buckle was worn at his back when he worked, was shoeing a pair of draught horses. Dick was working between forge and anvil. Sam Renshaw, the apprentice, was at the bellows. None spoke.

We saw the Remount man get off the tram at the stop opposite the smithy and cross the road. He was in uniform, a white lanyard, shining bandolier, riding breeches, puttees and boots that had been boned. He carried a bridle and leading rein. When he stopped a pace inside the smithy Dick looked up, did not answer the greeting but turned to Sam Renshaw and nodded. Sam went to the stables at the rear and came back with Billy Lad. Dick, hammer in one hand, tongs in the other, stood silent and motionless as the soldier fixed the bridle. The soldier said something which was left unanswered. Then he led the horse away. Mechanically, still holding the hammer and tongs, Dick followed to stand on the kerb's edge, quite motionless, watching and watching. His wife and daughter were at the parlour window. Mrs Dacre had the corner of her apron at her mouth, Katie a handkerchief under her nose. Dick did not stir until, far away, we saw the soldier and Billy Lad turn off at the main cross-section. Then Dick went back to the smithy door, threw tongs and hammer on to the earth floor, about faced and disappeared through the doors of the near-by pub.

Soon afterwards I was to have another lesson in the inadvisability of taking anybody and anything for granted in this precarious world.

Having just come downstairs, sleepy-eyed, at Mother's call to hurry for school, I, turning from washing myself at the sink, noticed the puzzling spectacle of three or four pools of blood on the cracked linoleum. Mother was at the table cutting bread. I put the towel aside and looked at her hands.

'Have you cut yourself, Mother?'

'No, lad. Why?' I pointed to the pools.

'Lord above!' she exclaimed, and looked at me anxiously: 'Are you all right?'

'Yes. I've only just come downstairs.'

She put the knife aside. We looked at each other then, once again at the pools. I saw another forming at her feet. 'Mother!' I exclaimed. 'It's you.'

She looked at her shoes, then lifted her skirts. A vein on her shin was fountaining blood in a forceful jet. 'Oh,' she said, vexed. 'It's that varicose vein. Run across to Mrs Boarder and ask her to come over for a minute.'

'God above!' Mrs Boarder said when I had babbled my tale. As we hurried back panic took hold of me. Suppose Mother were to die!

'This *is* a nice how-d'y'-do, this is,' Mrs Boarder said when she saw the bleeding. 'Looks as though somebody's been killing a pig. On the sofa with you, lass. Come on. No arguing. And you,' she added to me, 'off with you for the doctor.' Mother lay on the sofa; Mrs Boarder took the cushion from the rocking chair and stuffed it under Mother's heel. 'Now,' she said, 'where d'you keep your old bits o' sheets and things?' She saw that I hadn't stirred. 'You not gone yet? Away with you. Tell him it's urgent.' I ran.

The doctor prescribed an elastic bandage and a period of rest, ' … and you mustn't go back to work until I tell you.'

Marvellous! Mother at home all day. Actually in the house when we returned from school at noon and when lessons were finished for the day; a fire burning and a meal ready! There was, of course, the customary fly in the ointment. Three flies, in fact—no wages, no tips and, what was just as grievous, no bag. 'Never mind, kids,' she said, putting a brave face on things. 'Frugality of body and opulence of mind. And thank God we've got the piano money to fall back on.'

Until now she had been acquainted only with her children's behaviour on Sundays. She now decided that, while running wild during her absence at work, we had acquired what she considered to be rough and uncouth manners. Some of these faults stood naked and revealed and, offended

by our lapses into loutish gracelessness, she reminded us that
'You did not learn behaviour of that sort at home.' Her
watchful eyes did not miss a thing; even my table manners
came in for rebuke when one day, we were eating our one-
course meal. Exasperated, and using a handful of wooden
skewers to represent the full range of cutlery which we did
not possess, she laid, in front of me and in proper order, a
cover for an eight-course meal. 'There,' she said, indicating
the 'cutlery' for each successive course. 'There. That is for
your hors d'œuvre, that for soup, fish, entrée, joints and game,
salad, sweet, cheese.' I was instructed to 'work from the outside *inwards* to your plate.' In the unlikely event of my not wanting any one of the courses I was told to put the appropriate
knife and fork side by side in the centre of the plate ' ... and
the butler will understand. It does not mean that because
food is offered you have to consume it. Nothing is more
disgusting than gormandizing, a thing a *gen*tleman *never*
does. Have I made myself clear? Do you understand?' I
said that she had and that I did.

'Very well. And now you will know how to behave when
you are invited to a banquet.'

I heard sudden shouts of friends come to play in the street.
Without thinking I rose to join them and instantly was
rebuked: 'Have you not forgotten something?'

'Please may I leave the table?' I murmured, meekly.

'That is much better. And before you go off gallivanting
have you learned the Wordsworth poem?'

'Yes, Mother.'

'Then we will hear it. Proceed.'

I proceeded.

> ' ... Beside the lake, beneath the tree,
> Fluttering and dancing in the breeze.
> Conspicuous as the stars that shine
> And glitter in the milky way ... '

MY FATHER

'Walter.'

'Yes, Mother?'

' "Conspicuous"? "glitter"? Don't you mean "Continuous" and "twinkle"?' I held my tongue. Wordsworth's *Poetical Works* were taken from the bookcase and I was shown where I had misquoted. Afterwards I completed the poem to her satisfaction. 'Very good, lad. But you must learn to pay attention.' Wordsworth was replaced and the *Works of John Greenleaf Whittier* opened. 'There. That's the next you've to learn. *Barbara Frietchie*, and get something more worthwhile into that noddle of yours. You'll read it and you'll learn it and if you cannot recite it to me *without a mistake* by Saturday night ... Well, be warned, young man. Be warned. Now, you may go, and see that you don't get up to any mischief.'

Among the many sympathetic callers was Mr Wheelam. He said to my mother: 'It's a very good job it happened at home, by gum, it is. Why, if it'd have come on you while you were walking home at past midnight from one of those jobs of yours you could've dropped down in a dead faint from loss o' blood and bled to death in the street. And then', he went on, frowning as he looked at me, 'where would you and your sister have been?' His frown deepened. 'You are the Man of the House now and never you forget it. Yes, and what you ought to do is roll up those sleeves o' yours and get yourself a job that'll help to pay the rent. Why, when I was your age ... ' etc.

This was reasonable. I was the Man of the House just as other boys in like case whose spare-time jobs were bringing wages home.

A notice in a local pawnbroker's window announced that a smart lad who was a good handwriter and quick at figures was required. I did as the notice demanded and applied within.

The pawnbroker, a cadaverous gentleman with ill-fitting

artificial teeth which sometimes made castanet noises, gave me the twice-over, made a long 'Mmmm-ing' sound, then said dubiously: 'Not left school, eh?'

'Not yet, sir.'

'Handwriting good?'

'I think so, sir.'

Paper and pen were put on the counter. 'Write — er — Mrs Codlinham. Gent's suit. Three shillings. Put the shillings in figures.' He examined my writing and nodded. 'Three shillings is lent on the pledge,' he said. 'If the suit is bundled and put in a rack there is no charge for storing. If it's hung on a hanger there's a penny to pay. So let's say she has it hung. Then there's tuppence to pay for the ticket. Three shillings lent on the suit. How much does she get?'

'Two and ninepence, sir.'

He nodded, h'm-ed and ha-ed and stroked his chin: 'Still at school, eh? Oh, well. All right, then, Monday morning quarter to six, sharp, that's the time we open. Understand? Right. Now — quarter to six until — let's see. Start school at nine o'clock, don't you?'

'No, sir. Half past ten. They've taken over our school for the wounded soldiers.' I explained that ours shared another school's building on a shift system.

'I see. Well. Half an hour's allowed for your dinner when you're not at school. Nine o'clock we close Mondays, eight the other days. Half day Wednesday, Saturday night close at nine. What about wages, then?'

I said I did not know.

'Right. Two and six a week, fortnight's trial and see how you go on. Right?'

'Thank you, sir.'

I burst in on Mother with the news expecting an enthusiastic reception. She listened to my babbled tale, gave a little sigh and murmured: 'Never mind, laddie. Hope on, hope ever. One of these fine days my ship will come in.'

# 13

# *An Initiation*

---

In the blackness of the following Monday morning I was
outside the pawnshop before the appointed time. A solitary
light burned within. A bell began to ring across the road
calling the devout to early morning Mass. Mickmac and his
shawled, diminutive mother stopped by me. He said: 'Will
you hold me mother's bundle while we both go o'er to
church?' They turned. Holding the bundle I looked at the
church porch opposite. Through its open doors I saw the soft
and misty glow of many candles keeping the shadows at bay.
A youth came out of the darkness of the street. 'You the new
lad?' he asked, taking keys from his pocket. I said that I
was. He did not answer but opened the door. I followed
him in.

'What's that you've got?' He glanced at the bundle.

'Mrs McBride's. She's gone to church.'

'The old trick. Blarney. She'll take her turn just the same,
like the rest.' He blew his cheeks out. 'Another bloody week.'
He added, as the stuffy airlessness of the place hit us: 'Poooo!
Stink's enough to blind you.' He asked my name and when
I told him he replied: 'Reggie Sniblo, that's me. How old
are you?'

'Thirteen—next month.'

He shook his head as one despairing: 'Another six months
to go, before they'll let me join up.' He threw me an aggres-
sive look. 'But I'm not waitin'.' He touched his incipient
moustache. 'I'm tryin' agen, though, in a fortnight when this
has grown. When it's longer I ought to pass for eighteen any
time.' He pointed to a ladder aslant the big safe. 'See that?
Always got to be left there just like it is now. Police orders.

If it's been shifted they know there's summat wrong. Come on.' We went into the pledge office at the back where he lit the gas, ignoring the loud chorus of women in the back yard shouting to be admitted. Iron bars protected the windows. 'In here,' he said, without looking to see if I followed. We traversed every room in the premises, upstairs and down, to light the gas brackets. Storage racks were everywhere all stuffed with bundles, a ticket pinned to each. Even the fire-place in the pledge office was blocked to accommodate more racks. We finished the tour in a small and dismal kitchen whose distempered walls were leprous with damp. A small battered kettle, a white pint pot and a tin saucepan stood near a gas-ring on the bare table. Near the latter was a solitary windsor chair.

Reggie put what I guessed to be a packet of sandwiches on the table, hung his raincoat and hat on a nail behind the door and said, as he took a newspaper from the raincoat's pocket, 'You eat in here.' He glanced at the newspaper. 'See,' he said, dolefully, 'we've made *another* muckin' advance. Bloody war'll be over afore I get there.' He looked at me, aggrieved. 'Just my luck, you'll see.' I followed as he trudged back to the pledge office, ignoring once again the demands from the yard. There was a hammering on the window pane. The irate, booming voice of Mrs Boarder was unmistakable. 'Open the soddin' door, you titty-eyed, ginger-haired get. There's some poor old buggers out here frozen stiff.'

'That's Annie,' he said. 'Tek no notice.'

In the alcove to the right of the chimney breast was a high desk pushed against the pledge-stuffed racks and, with it, a high stool. From under the desk-flap Reggie took a movable date stamp and a sheaf of blank, perforated pawntickets. 'Here you are,' he said. 'He shouts out the name and address, then what she's pawned and how much for. You write it in the book, then you copy it all out agen on the tickets.' He began to stamp the tickets, conversing as he worked: 'She

keeps one ticket and the other he pins on the bundle.' He
baffled me for a second when, interrupting his work, he
grabbed a pin from a tin on the desk: the pins were longer
and of heavier gauge than the domestic article. 'You would,
would you, you bastard,' he exclaimed and made a thrust at
one of the bundles in the rack by the desk. 'Take that.' He
turned to me with a self-satisfied nod and showed me the
impaled bug. 'Keep your eyes open for 'em,' he warned.
'They'll have you—specially of a Monday mornin' when
they're starvin'. Fifteen, that's the most I've ever had on one
pin. How much is he payin' you?'

I told him. Whatever comment he might have been about
to make was interrupted by the arrival of our employer who
grunted in answer to our 'Good morning, sir.' The multitude
outside resumed its clamour, but it was not until the boss had
removed his wrappings and hung them up that he said, 'Go
on, then. Let them in.' Taking keys from his pocket he went
to the safe.

Reggie gave me a push. 'Go on, then. Let 'em in. And', he
warned as I shinned over the counter, 'watch out when
you've pulled that bottom bolt or you'll be trampled to
death.' As I shot back the door's top bolt I saw the latch rise.
The noise without now resembled that at a football match.
Even this was exceeded when I kicked the bottom bolt back,
the door was flung wide and I had to fly out of the way of a
stampede of shawled and clogged women, aprons bulging
with things to be pawned. Mrs Boarder was in the van and,
by the time I had reached the safety of the counter's other
side, she and those at the front had piled their stuff on the
counter like revolutionaries throwing up a barricade. Mrs
Boarder's contribution extended the counter's width and it
was heaped so high that it quite concealed her daughter
Hetty who had helped carry some of the burden. The shop
was packed, spilling into the backyard. Without a glance at
his customers the pawnbroker came from the safe carrying

three canvas bags. He was followed by Reggie, acolyte-fashion, bearing the leather-bound book of account. Everybody watched the silver and copper being poured into the till's compartments and the paper money placed at the back.

'Now,' the pawnbroker said, at which Mrs Boarder slowly took her large hand from a flat, brown-paper package, closed her left eye and said, out of the right-hand corner of her mouth, 'The usual,' then she coughed, reached for her Spanish comb and scratched her crown.

The pawnbroker took the package into the front shop into which, with the exception of Reggie and me, none could see. I saw him take out and count several old-age pension books and 'ring papers', documents issued to servicemen's wives and mothers for payment of allowances at post offices. On each was a printed warning to pawnbrokers and money-lenders not to accept them as security for loans. He put them into the safe, came back to the pledge office and said, 'Mrs Boarder. Goods. Two and six. Fifteen times.'

Reggie set me the task of writing the tickets while he made the entries in the account book. Mrs Boarder pushed a man's suit over the counter. 'Fifteen shillings,' she said, her dark eyes on the pawnbroker as though assessing his mood.

'Mrs Boarder. Gent's suit. Seven and six,' he called out.

'Oh, go on with you,' Mrs Boarder protested. 'She'll play Hamlet with me, will my customer. Make it twelve and a tanner.'

'Seven and six,' he said relentlessly. 'Fraying at the turn-ups.'

Mrs Boarder pouted. 'Oh, like that, eh?' she said, huffily adding, half turning to the others, 'He's seen his arse agen this morning.'

A buzz went round, commenting on the pawnbroker's stingy attitude. Still frowning, Mrs Boarder pushed across a bulging collection of wearing apparel wrapped in a print apron. 'I want five bob on that and not a penny less or I'll take 'em round to Phillip's.' He examined each item. 'Clean clothes, five shillings,' he said.

I wrote the tickets, Reggie did the book-keeping and pinned the counterfoils to each particular pledge, then either he or I grabbed the bundle and nipped off smartly to lodge it in one of the racks at the back of the shop.

It went on incessantly; the place still was full even when, on glancing through the dirty barred window, I could see the meagre light of morning silhouetting the dark roofs and smoking chimneypots. It was only half past eight. Still another hour and a half before I would be free.

Soon after nine the tide ebbed awhile. The pawnbroker, on guard over the cash drawer, said, without turning, 'Very well, Sniblo,' at which Reggie opened a small cupboard under the counter and took out teapot, cup, saucer, spoon and a small jug. Our employer went to his overcoat and came back with a tissue-papered package and an apple. He took a penny from the till and passed this and the jug to me saying: 'Milk. Make haste. Make haste.' When I returned he was standing at the counter eating, I noticed, cheese-and-tomato sandwiches. He poured tea, then directed Reggie and me to remove the pile of suits that had been heaped on the far corner of the counter.

We lugged them upstairs where, because of the rows of stuffed racks, every sound was muffled. 'I'm having five minutes,' Reggie said and leaned against a doorless cupboard near one of the windows, the glazing of the lower halves of which was painted brown. Here and there in the paint peep-holes had been scratched. He lit a cigarette, then began to pull the hairs on his top lip: 'You *can* see 'em, can't you?' he asked in tones that pleaded for confirmation. I assured him that they were indeed noticeable.

'Givin' 'em Vaseline every night,' he said. 'Lashin' it on.' He sighed, then looked at me. 'What time d'you go to school?'

'Half ten. But I've got to have my breakfast first.'

'It's all right for you,' he mumbled, morosely. 'School— and out of here. It's a break. Stuck here, me. Nine o'clock tonight.' He sighed again and blew out his cheeks. 'D'you know,' he said, 'I wanted to go on the stage. Fred Karno's troupe. Did you know that? But she wouldn't let me. Got me into this job here. "Job for life," that's what my ma said.' He shook his head and a faraway look came into his eyes. 'Fred Karno's. Being with 'em. Going on trains. A different town every week. And look at me. A soddin' prisoner in here.' With sudden animation he said, 'Like me to give you an imitation? Gus Elen? George Lashwood? Marie Lloyd? He' y' are, then. Harry Champion … ' He began singing, *sotto voce*:

'Just a week or two ago my poor old Uncle Bill
Went and kicked the bucket, and he left me in his will.
The other day I popped around to see poor Auntie Jane,
She said, "Your Uncle Bill has left to you a watch and
    chain."

'I put it on, right across me vest, thought I looked a
    dandy as it dangled on me chest.
Just to flash it off I started walking round about,
A lot of kiddies followed me and all began to shout:
"Any old iron. Any old i … " '

'Sniblo.' A sepulchral voice from below interrupted the performance. He made a wry face and a rude gesture savagely towards the stairs, but obeyed the call.

When it was a few minutes off ten I reminded my employer of the time.

'Very well,' he said. 'And allow yourself half an hour for your dinner. Back here sharp on time. Are all the lights turned off upstairs, Sniblo?'

I did not wait to hear the answer.

# 14

# Staff Shortage and High Drama

Weekdays were bad enough, but to be imprisoned in the pawnshop until nine o'clock of a Saturday night was excruciating. I knew the time when, on this night, my friends would be off and away. Around seven o'clock, peering through the peepholes of the shop's upstairs windows, I watched them all go by in a chattering, happy bunch. Nobby, Mickmac, the Seeley brothers and Alfie off to the excitement of Manchester's live poultry market at Shudehill and the entertaining cheap-jack stalls and quack doctors of Smithfield.

It was small consolation to know that Reggie was in worse case than me. He was stuck here all day and every day whereas, on weekdays, I at least had the escape to school. However, one Thursday morning when I arrived at the shop as the clock was striking six I found Reggie already within. He greeted me triumphantly and threw both hands in the air. 'They've taken me!' he shouted. 'I'm a soldier!' He then went through the rifle drill, finishing with a shoulder arms and a smart salute. 'Can you see it? Me — out there with the boys!' Before I could answer he began to strut four paces to the left then four to the right, ruler for swagger cane under his arm, a wink and a twiddle of his moustache while singing:

'Ho! Maddeymowsell from Armenteers, Paaaarley Voo,
Ha! Maddeymowsell from Armen ... '

The performance ended abruptly. Our employer regarded Reggie coldly.

'Morning, sir,' Reggie said. 'They've took me. I'm a soldier.' He stood there, beaming.

'Oh?' the pawnbroker said, the corners of his mouth falling. 'When do you go?'

'Monday morning, report at the barracks,' Reggie said, still grinning.

'You ought to have given me notice. A week's notice at least,' the pawnbroker said on a plaintive note. 'This puts the business in a very awkward position. After all —' he inclined his head towards me, '*he*'s not left school yet.'

'I can't help that,' Reggie said, indignant that his answering the call to arms should be held in such light esteem. This was the first time that I had seen colour in his pale cheeks. 'I've got to do my bit like everybody else, havn' I?'

Both sulked but, later, when we were alone together, Reggie said: 'He can go to hell and back to see how far it is. But I'll tell you this: I'm off o' Monday mornin' and finish with this stinkin' hole, aye, and I'm never comin' back.'

We shook hands outside the shop late on Saturday night. He said that he would write.

His place was not filled and, in consequence, I had his work to do in addition to my own. It never occurred to my employer to raise my pay accordingly. When I hinted that for my part this would be most acceptable he shook his head slowly and said, gloomily: 'You haven't sufficient experience yet and you are only working half-time. There's a war on, remember. However, we'll see what we can do when you leave school. Bad,' he concluded, still shaking his head. 'Things are bad. Very bad.' But for whom he did not say.

He was soon advised. Wives and mothers of soldiers gone off to the war found something else missing — their menfolk's wages. My employer was beneficiary and, as his business boomed, he inclined more and more to cheeseparing in the matter of his loans.

The redoubtable Mrs Boarder elected herself spokeswoman for all among his customers who were dissatisfied.

'Get on with you, you bloody old miser,' she cried, eyes

burning. 'You'd have the skin off our backs. Look—' She thrust her hand into her vast bosom, pulled out her army allotment papers and slapped them on the counter. 'There,' she said. 'Look for yourself. That's what a soldier's dependants have to live on. Go on, then. Look. A tanner a flamin' day for a wife and a penny for each chile. Then you come cuttin' down on everythin' we pawn. Profiteerin', that's what it is, while they're out there in the soddin' trenches.' There was a chorus of mumbled agreement.

'There's no cause to be abusive, Mrs Boarder,' he said.

'Abusive? Don't you start gettin' on to me or I'll wipe you one across the kisser.' She put her arm protectively across the shoulder of Mickmac's mother whose thin face, sharp nose and scrawny neck scarcely rose above counter height, while with her free hand she pointed to Mrs McBride's pledge about which the dispute revolved. 'Eighteen-pence on a pair o' blankets, a quilt and their Theresa's confirmation dress? You ought to be ashamed of yourself, my Christ, you ought.'

'All right, then. All right,' he said irritably and turned to me: 'Make it half a crown.' This helped to mollify the customers; the buzz of their protesting conversation subsided, though the war between Mrs Boarder and my employer did not diminish.

One of the many pledges which she made as a regular weekly habit was the pair of running pumps belonging her absent soldier son. These pumps, tightly wrapped and pinned in a square of old cotton print had their spikes sticking outward. She slipped these across the counter towards the end of her manifold transactions. 'The usual,' she said, then pushed the next transaction across.

The pawnbroker, feeling the spikes, called out: 'Running pumps, two and six,' sent the bundle sliding down the counter, then pulled towards him the next item.

This morning the pumps were pushed across, the details called out, but, as the bundle went sliding along the counter, the pin became detached, the wrapping fell away and there, in all its nakedness, the bundle's guilty secret stood discovered to all in the crowded shop.

Silence. You could hear the sparrows chirping outside.

The pawnbroker, like everybody else except Mrs Boarder and her daughter Hetty, stared at the two pieces of cardboard cut to the size and shape of the running pumps' soles. 'Wild Woodbine Cigarettes' the printing said on the cardboard. Half-inch nails protruded at appropriate places, the space between the cardboard stuffed with newspaper and the whole secured with string round toe, heel and instep.

Excusably, perhaps, the pawnbroker was guilty of a daft utterance. 'What's this?' he said. There was neither sound nor movement from anybody except Hetty Boarder whose nose required the aid of a handkerchief. She sniffled, loudly.

Two spots of pink the size of sixpences stained the pawnbroker's cheeks. He stared at Mrs Boarder, she at him. A new expression appeared on his face. All other business was suspended as he turned and instructed me to go back through the ledger and extract the ticket numbers of every transaction to do with 'Running pumps, two and six.' This I did, then he and I, rummaging through the racks at the back of the shop, returned to the counter each with an impressive collection, all of which, when opened in front of the cool culprit and astounded audience, proved to be exactly as that which had given the game away.

'Come into the front shop,' the pawnbroker ordered magisterially. Mrs Boarder about faced, pushed her way through the awed crowd, daughter following, went round to the front shop and, without the least sign of penitence, boldly faced her accuser.

From my desk I had the advantage of seeing and hearing all that went on. Denied this the excited customers began to bombard me with urgent whispers: 'What're they doin'? What's he sayin'?'

'What am I going to do?' the pawnbroker demanded with the injured air of someone of whom unfair advantage had been taken.

'That I neither know nor care,' Mrs Boarder retorted. Her hauteur was impressive. She raised her voice, adding, with what I now know to be an eye on the gallery: '*You* try feedin' a tribe o' kids on a soldier's allotment wi' things the price they are.'

'Oh, I see,' he replied, eyes popping. '*That* is to be the attitude, is it? Well, Mrs Boarder, in that case I shall have to bring the matter to the attention of the police ... '

'And in that case,' she interrupted, stabbing an accusative finger in the direction of the safe, '*I* shall have to tell 'em about all the old-age pension books and ring papers you've got stuffed in there.' In case he might have it in mind to repudiate these illegal transactions she, striking the counter with her palm as though slapping down a trump card, raised the volume of her booming voice as she cried: 'I've got all the tickets, remember, and when it gets in the newspapers let's see how it goes down with all them bible-punchers that go to that chapel o' yours. Get on, you preaching bleeder, you, aye, and all you stand for. You lot'll not be happy till you've milked us dry.' He made a stammering attempt at reply but she would have none of it. 'Waste no more time, man.' She jerked her thumb towards the pledge office. 'Back in there and let's get finished. Another thing,' she warned, 'if you come this lark again trying to show me up in front of everybody I'll take all my custom somewhere else.' She swept about face and, forgetting that Hetty was standing behind her, tripped and stumbled over her daughter. Recovering balance she began to slap the girl, backhand and palm across both ears, pushing her forward and declaring: 'All your flamin' fault, not puttin' that pin in proper. That's a regular half-dollar a week gone, you faggot, you. Haven't I got enough troubles and worries on my mind?'

Without closing the door she returned to the pledge office, Spanish comb askew. Setting this straight and wearing the indignant expression of one convinced that she was the victim of a bare-faced fraud, she huffily collected her dues then swept out majestically through the awed and respectful crowd.

# 15
# *Jubilation*

---

Now that Reggie was gone I got, during slack periods, a whiff of the torture a prisoner endures when condemned to solitary confinement.

The pawnbroker never had anything to say by way of conversation. When waiting for custom he stood in front of the till staring at the opposite wall like a stalled horse while I, pin in hand, kept my eyes alert for famished bugs emerging from the bundled stuff piled round my desk. Although he seemed to be lost in thought my employer always knew when, silently, I spread the latest issue of my favourite boys' magazine on the ledger.

'Racks,' he said, by which I knew him to mean, 'Put the reading matter away and occupy yourself straightening the pledges.'

I always made it convenient to begin upstairs where I could dawdle by the paint-obscured windows and look upon freedom through the peep-holes, or I might treat myself to a musical interlude. The doorless cupboard by the chimney breast housed pledges of an odd nature, kits of workmen's tools, dockers' hooks, cut-throat razors and a solitary gramophone which had a big horn. With this were a couple of single-sided records, vocal numbers, with orchestral accompaniment, by the Irish tunesmith Mr Michael William Balfe who, among other works, had to his credit the ever-popular opera, *The Bohemian Girl*. That there weren't any gramophone needles was of small account. Tool kits were handy and there was no shortage of pins. Stuffing a bundle down the horn I listened to the muffled renderings of:

> I dreamt that I dwelt in marble halls
> with vassals and serfs at my side ...

or the affecting and touching strains of:

> When other lips and other hearts
> Their tale of love shall tell ...

in which, with suitable actions, I joined until the Voice from
below called my name.

Once a month came the great exodus of unredeemed
pledges. These having lain undisturbed for the legal year and
a day became the pawnbroker's property. It was my duty
to lug these from the racks, pile them on the counter in the
front shop while a swarthy market-stall dealer in the second-
hand, with shrugs, shoulder-raisings, showing of palms and
despairing glances heavenwards, haggled and bargained.
Also once a month the pawnbroker received his sleeping
partner. This, an elderly man, crept rather than walked.
He listened to the pawnbroker's report with the manner of
one trying hard to believe the tale he was being told.
Afterwards they conferred in whispers as they went over the
books; then, with heads almost touching, appraised the unredeemed pledges in the jewellery line. During this, those
who came to pawn were made to wait while careful consideration was given to each item, whether there would be
more profit by putting it into the window as 'Bargain.
Unredeemed Pledge', or selling it to people in Manchester
who dealt in these things.

The people waiting in the pledge office stood there
patiently and resigned or, to save time, left their bundles
on the counter in order of precedence while going on other
business. All asked me to 'Keep your eye on it, lad.' This
day, when the active and passive partners in the front shop
were whispering over the gold and silver valuables that now
were theirs, my sole companions in the pledge office were

Hetty Boarder and Mickmac. They had been left on guard.
Mickmac, bored, was showing off. Movable date-stamp in
hand I interrupted my work at the counter to look at his
dirty bare feet and scabby bow legs passing to and fro on
the counter's other side as he walked on his hands. He was
able to keep up this enviable accomplishment over impressive
periods.

Hetty, who was sitting on the counter, was unimpressed by
these gymnastics. She wore an air of preoccupation, absently
picked up the date-stamp and idly revolved the cylinder
which governed the years. She pressed it into the pad, then
made an impression on the back of her hand. 'Ooo! See!'
she said, extending her hand. The date read 'Sept 15 1921'.
She looked at me, awed. '1921!' she murmured. 'I wonder
what we'll be doin' then.' She sighed, heavily: 'I know what
I want to do when I leave school.' I listened. She threw me a
sulky look: 'Steam laundry. That's where me mother wants
me to go. Says I've *got* to.' I made sympathetic noises.

Puzzlingly, she said, her expression changing: 'I wonder
where he is.'

'Who?'

'Reggie.'

'Do you mean Reggie Sniblo?'

She stared at me as one affronted: 'O' course I mean him.'
She smiled and I wished my teeth were as strong and as
white as hers. 'Did you ever see him do Charlie Chaplin and
Harry Champion?' She put her head back, clapped her palm
to her mouth and laughed.

'*I* can do Charlie Chaplin,' Mickmac said. 'Look.' He
began to shuffle around, splay-footed, twisting his top lip
from side to side and twirling an imaginary cane.

'Oh, shurrup, you,' Hetty said, contemptuously. She went
on, morosely, her dark eyes glowing. 'He wanted to go on the
stage, too. He told our Harry.'

'Do you mean *you* want to go on the stage?' I was amazed.

4

Hetty, who had outgrown her clothes, who was neither schoolgirl nor young woman, who, though she always led the other girls in the street singing and dancing round the barrel organs, yet was just as much at home with us lads in our rough street games. My incredulity must have wounded her; her chin sank slowly on her chest, then, recovering herself, her manner changed. 'I'll show you,' she said, defiantly. She slipped off the counter. 'See here. Vesta Tilley.' Just as she had struck the preliminary pose the pledge-office door was flung wide and her mother, agog, burst in. She had her left hand at her mouth and was sucking hard at a finger as though this had been cut. 'Gerrout o' the way,' she cried, fetching Hetty a clout which sent her sprawling into Mickmac's arms then, still sucking, she began to fist the counter. Mrs McBride was behind her: she, too, was breathless and excited. 'Where are you, then?' Mrs Boarder bawled, leaning over the counter trying to look into the front shop. Affronted, his brows arched, mouth slightly open, the pawnbroker came as though to chide. 'Damn and blast,' Mrs Boarder exploded as she tugged at her wedding ring. 'Here,' she went on, turning to Mrs McBride, 'you go first, lass,' then, to my employer, as Mrs McBride slipped the wedding ring from her skeletonic finger, 'A quid each we want on our rings and quick about it. Aye, and there'll be more of 'em to come before this day's much older.' She screwed up her face as she forced her ring over her knuckle. 'There!' she said, on a great exhalation as the ring came free.

'I'm very busy. You'll have to wait ... ' the pawnbroker began.

'You're not as busy as us,' she retorted. 'Telegrams've just come. All of 'em 've got seven days' leave and they're on their way.' She slapped the ring down. 'Let's be havin' the ready and never mind muckin' about with the acid test. Eighteen carat, solid, the pair of 'em, and stamped inside.

Aye, and never been off before since we were wed. Those lads're going to have a welcome they'll never forget.'

They were gone and away, in no time to be succeeded by other bustling wives who could not transact their business quickly enough. They took their excitement away with them leaving me strait-jacketed in a torturing fret, teased by the jeering clock-face and its dragging fingers.

When I was released to go to school I damned consequences, played the truant and dashed for home.

Transformation scene! From one end of our street to the other, lines of coloured tissue-paper pennants at bedroom height crossed from house to house. Flags on poles hung out of windows and at the street's head a huge, billowing banner, WELCOME HOME. Every front door wide; women rushing in and out: trestle tables borrowed from somewhere and placed end to end in the middle of the roadway. Half a dozen men in shirtsleeves lugging the piano through the doors of the Spinners' Arms on to the pavement.

Everywhere effervescence—and the leaking of a secret. Bert Harrington and Katie Dacre were to be married.

Soon after five o'clock, boys who had been standing sentinel at the tram stop came rushing into the street screeching: 'They're here! They're here!' Bandsmen, instruments at the ready, came out of the pub, formed a circle in the middle of the road junction and struck up 'See the Conquering Hero'.

There they came with rifles, bayonets, tin hats, kit-bags and uniforms caked with Flanders mud. Pat McBride, Mr Boarder and Harry, Dick Dacre, Bert Harrington and Reggie Sniblo. All changed, all pallor gone, red-faced and brawny, serjeant's stripes on Bert's arm. There they came to be engulfed amid the general tumult.

Passers-by crowding both ends of the street; press photographers hanging out of bedroom windows as the *al fresco* banquet was served. The food gone, tables removed, the piano struck up as the barrels of beer were broached and the participants gave themselves up to jigging and dancing, a high and heady revel that seemed without end until, by slow degrees, people began to slip away. Doors closed, lights disappeared and in the empty quietude, the night silence was broken only by the forest rustlings of the tissue pennants.

# 16

# Corn in Egypt

---

The doctor was insistent: ' ... and you must find lighter work and give up all those extra jobs ... ' The extra jobs on which Mother relied had come to an abrupt end. Banquets and suchlike were 'out for the duration'.

'Ay, dear-o-dear,' she said and scratched the nape of her neck which was her habit when perplexed. 'How *are* we going to manage?' Soon I would be entering my thirteenth year, an age when, if I passed the Labour Examination, I could finish at school and bring home full-time wages.

Fortune smiled, Mother found a less demanding job in a small restaurant attached to the headquarters of a non-conformist religious organization in the heart of Manchester. The customers here, mostly parsons and university professors, were not, unfortunately, as free with tips as had been the businessmen at the other place. Where Mother was concerned this disappointment was more than compensated by advantages in other ways.

Incorporated in the building was a spacious hall, galleried and platformed. Primarily it was for the use of nonconformist conferences and meetings but was hired out for other purposes. Among those of the latter who used the hall were, in Mother's view, the kings and queens of mankind in the persons of star performers of visiting opera companies, instrumentalists of international reputation, prima ballerinas and the august Hallé Orchestra itself on those occasions when its home, the Free Trade Hall, was not available for rehearsals. All these idols were permitted use of the restaurant, and the extra-special attention they received at Mother's hands produced for her, in turn, a flow of complimentary tickets to riches beyond the calculation of this money-grubbing world.

Nor did the change of job mean deprivation for our necessitous neighbours. The contents of 'the bag' were still forthcoming and, as the war's effect on larders began to make itself felt, these windfalls became more and more precious.

It now was a case of 'first come first served' where shopping was concerned. When the restricted supplies had gone, SOLD OUT notices were daubed on shop windows and those who called to buy on their way home from work were, in the matter of essentials, sent empty away. Mother's problem here was solved by Mrs Boarder who, by way of thanks for gifts from 'the bag', deputized for Mother at the butcher's. On the matter of newspaper reports of food shortages Mrs Boarder was scathing. 'Food shortages!' she scoffed. 'Telling us! And what in hell's name is new about that in these parts, war or no war? "Over by Christmas"! But which one, that's what I'd like to know. And now to cap it all I'm in the family way again and me thinkin' I'd finished.' She looked at my mother, fetched a great sigh and shook her head. Mother did likewise. Mrs Boarder continued: 'I'm nearly the colour of pennyroyal but it's no use. How the hell am I goin' to manage to keep another mouth on soldier's pay?' She opened her purse and tipped its contents on to her palm. 'There. Look at it. Fourpence ha'penny and only Wednesday. Friday afore I draw agen at the post office. Magicians, that's what they must think we are.'

'Never mind, Annie, love,' Polly Mytton murmured, soothingly. 'We've pulled through hard times before.' She cleared her throat, took a deep breath and softly began to sing: 'He shall feed His flock, like a Shepherd ... '

Instead of consoling, this provoked Mrs Boarder: 'He's takin' His time,' she interrupted. 'The sooner He starts performin' round here the better.' She was frowning. 'Anyway, our Hetty's leaving school and she'll be bringing

wages home.' Her frown deepened. 'I'll give that faggot
"stage".' She raised her brows indignantly. 'Yes. Stage.
That's her ladyship if you please. Everlastingly stuck in front
of the mirror making faces and powdering up. And where is
she when I want her? Regent Theatre, stage door, standing
there gawping like a moon-struck calf. O' course, I blame
her uncle, encouraging her. Scene-shifter there. No right to
let her in, hasn't our Fred.'

'Go on with you, woman,' Polly said. 'She's young, that's
all. She'll get over it.'

'You bet she will,' Mrs Boarder said, emphatically. 'That
young madam's going to work in the steam laundry and like
it. She thinks she can do anything she's a mind because her
dad's away.' She thrust out her hand, her sole wealth was
still in her palm. 'Penny a day, that's the allowance they
make me for her keep. Aye, and eggs gone up to sixpence
each.'

'Get a few hens like I'm doing, Annie, and stick 'em in the
backyard,' Polly said, adding, 'And I only wish I'd a piece
of land, I'd grow all my own vegetables.'

'Listen to the woman!' Mrs Boarder said. She rattled her
fourpence halfpenny. 'I'll just nip off to Shudehill Market
and buy half a dozen.' She laughed: 'You see that those hens
o' yours're locked up at night, Polly. The way things're
going in the food line there'll be some two-legged foxes over
your backyard wall when it's dark.'

'A crying shame,' Mother said. 'Evil, it is, the way these
profiteers are being allowed to make their fortunes.'

'Aye,' Mrs Boarder agreed, bitterly. 'The butchers, the
grocers, every man-jack of 'em with a shop coining it. My
God! It makes my blood boil, that it does.'

The simmering discontent exploded spontaneously
throughout the land. Newspaper headlines trumpeted news
of atrocity on the high seas. The *Lusitania*, an unarmed liner,
torpedoed and sunk off the Old Head of Kinsale with a loss

of one thousand one hundred and ninety-eight passengers and crew, a hundred and twenty-four neutral Americans among the former. In every town, in every city 'the mob' emerged: its quarry, shopkeepers who were unfortunate enough to have foreign-sounding names, which for the dark purpose of the nefarious were interpreted as German.

It must have been the afternoon of a Wednesday or I would not have been at liberty from the pawnshop. My memory finds further confirmation in the recollection of the butchers' shops being closed. The men of blood did not finish their gory business until late Wednesday morning when their shops were hanging with the dripping carcases of the animals purchased at Tuesday's market. These, and festoons of sausages, were on display for sale first thing Thursday morning.

Ahead of me was a milling, clamorous crowd in front of Hoffman's butcher's shop. Mr Hoffman, German-born, a naturalized British subject of many years' standing and a popular patron among the regulars of the Hare and Hounds pub, was well known for the quality of his sausages, pies and products of the pig, cooked and otherwise.

He was not to be seen. Within and without his place of business the mob, mostly women, shouted, surged and swayed. The windows were gone, the shop door shattered. Through this Mrs Boarder emerged wild-eyed and victorious holding a hefty ham in one hand and a double link of sausages a yard and more long in the other. As she pushed her way out a man was endeavouring to push his way in. Ill-advisedly he made a grab to wrest the ham from her. Outraged she brought up her knee and, as his mouth contorted in agony, she fetched him an unholy whack on the head with the ham, then she, her deep voice bawling, 'Out of my way. Out of my way,' cleared a path for herself with both elbows to where Hetty was standing on the mob's fringe. 'Here, you,' she cried and, wedging the ham between her knees bit off a

generous length of the sausages. She then whipped the
Spanish comb from her hair and stabbed every one of the
sausages. 'Quick,' she ordered, slapping them into Hetty's
hands. 'Round with 'em to your grandma's. In the frying
pan with 'em and if I hear you've let 'em burn I'll have the
skin off your arse.' Then she was off with the remaining
sausages and the ham concealed under her shawl. The shop
was cleared. The crowd of the empty-handed that were
within joined the one that was outside. All wore the same
expression of baffled fury appropriate to punters discovering
that they have been welshed by an absconding bookie.

Above the tumult a voice bawled, 'Scheiners!' and
repeated, 'Scheiners!' Instantly the frustrated crowd clattered away to form an ever-growing arc round the double-
fronted corner shop's windows whose fascia boards, in
addition to the owner's name, announced: 'Drapers, Out-
fitters and Milliners. Est. 1889'. Placatingly and in whitewash capitals, the apprehensive proprietor had hurriedly
inscribed WE ARE POLES on his windows.

The crowd's menacing roar was directed at the upstairs
rooms where the owner had his living quarters. A lace curtain
was seen to move slightly: fingers pointed and fists were
shaken at it. Among the catcalls hurled at the upper windows
the name of the torpedoed liner was constantly invoked. The
stentorian voice of Mrs Boarder proclaimed her reappearance
and, as usual, she was at the centre and in the forefront of
things. 'Atrocities,' she bawled. 'Women and children ... '
The rest of her utterance was lost in an uproar of jeering.
An old lady wearing a disintegrating black straw bonnet and
a threadbare shawl which was pinned under her chin took a
step forward from the crowd and, with face contorted as she
shouted something, hurled an empty condensed-milk tin at
the plate-glass windows. It bounced off harmlessly. Immediately it was succeeded by a fusillade of half-bricks and the
showering crash of the shattered windows. The crowd surged

forward with a horrid roar and kicked in what was left of the glass: all and everybody burned with a consuming desire of lust for loot.

Every article in the windows was gone in minutes. Inside, shelves, stock boxes, counter displays and store-rooms were laid bare. A solitary policeman stood helpless and conspicuous on the pavement, his futile words falling upon the deaf as the heavily-laden burgesses forced their way out of the press. 'You'll have it to pay for,' he prophesied. 'It'll all come out of the rates.'

My employer and I were kept hard at it all the next day. His newspaper carried pictures of the 'anti-German riots'. He did not pass any comment on the fact that everything pushed to him was brand new, some items even still having their price tickets pinned to them by way of evidence of value. He was unimpressed; the loans he offered were minimal and, though productive of indignant protestations, none was refused. He also knew that none was likely to be redeemed and that, after a year and a day, the goods would be transferred from the racks for display in the sales department at full and current retail price.

# 17
# *A Job for Life*

My headmaster was asking me questions at random such as what the product was of seven multiplied by nine. The quiz constituted the 'Labour Examination' ordained by the Board of Education. It was open to fatherless boys who, if they passed, could finish with schooling prematurely and go to work full time. When I had satisfied him he held out his hand and said, 'Well, you are now setting out in life. Be a good boy, do your best, work hard and good luck.' We shook hands. I ran into the schoolyard, capered about and shouted, joyously: 'I've left! I've left!'

On the Saturday night of my first full week of employment my employer was afflicted with amnesia. Soon after nine o'clock, when I had bolted the back doors and turned off all lights except that above the safe, I looked at the half crown he had given me and said to him: 'I'm working full time now, sir.'

'H'm!' he said as though the reminder were something of an impertinence. He repeated 'H'm!' adding 'Ye-es.' He gave the matter some thought, then looked at me. 'We mustn't forget you aren't fourteen yet. Still only a schoolboy, really.' He then looked at the floor, pulled his lip and frowned. 'Er—um. Yes,' he told the floor. 'Fifty per cent,' he went on, glancing at me. 'Let's say three and sixpence a week —ah?' He gave me another shilling which, my mother assured me, was 'a godsend'.

Now being fully employed I nursed the hope that my employer would exhibit the 'Smart Boy Wanted' card in the window, thus not only providing my vanity with a subordinate but also, and what was more important, giving me a companion with whom I could converse during the desert periods when trade was slack. He seemed quite content to leave things as they were.

Revelation came. During the endlessness of Monday's fifteen hours I saw the iron bars of the backyard windows though different eyes. I was in a trap. There came back to me Reggie's mournful words: 'It's all right for you. School—and out of it. Stuck here, me. Nine o'clock tonight.'

Resentfully my heart stirred, sullenly rebellious against the shop's corroding tedium and its suffocating oppression. The spirit of the place became personified, a malevolent thing shrouded in black that lurked in the pledge-stuffed and muffled alcoves above or, on my approach, withdrew silently to merge with shadows in the shop's back rooms.

The half-day holiday of a Wednesday was a mockery, the streets empty of my friends. Saturday, as always, was derisive, I at work until past nine o'clock, a time when the street lads were thinking of returning from the excitements of their Manchester adventurings.

Unexpectedly my pawnshop days were brought to an abrupt end by an insect. Science has classified this by the name of *Pediculus humanus-corporis*, though the great un-learned know it, among other names, as the body louse. Unhappily at this time Science was unaware that for many years it possessed in its armoury a most powerful weapon against *Pediculus* and other insect pests which scourged humanity throughout the world. In 1874 a Mr Zeidler had prepared a chemical compound with the jaw-breaking name of Dichlorodiphenyltrichloroethane. It lay unused until 1939 when a Mr Müller in Switzerland discovered its powerful insecticidal qualities. He called it by the abbreviated name by which it now is known to us all, that is D.D.T.

Having discovered that I was playing host to the parasites my mother presented herself at the counter of the pawn-shop's sales department in a state of what I can only describe as 'high dudgeon'. The indignant manner with which she carried on to my employer might well have given anybody the impression that I had contracted the undesirables from him.

Instead of deprecating the insulting implication he astonished me, but not my mother, by saying, airily: 'Oh, when *I* get home I go to the bathroom, take a bath and change into clean things.'

At this Mother exploded, remarking that our bath hung from a nail on the backyard wall and, furthermore, my wardrobe did not permit of a daily change of the necessaries.

She was still fuming when we entered our street where we met Mrs Boarder. 'Oh, them?' Mrs Boarder said and laughed. 'A present from Flanders, that's what those are.' She followed us into our house and sat on the chair by the door. 'My husband and our Harry were walking alive when they came home on leave.' She began to scratch herself. 'Makes me itch to think about it. They used to say they were a sign of good health. Puh! Tell you, lass, every stitch of their uniforms on the table and me and our Hetty went along every seam with a lighted taper. My God! As though the poor lads haven't got enough to put up with in those trenches.'

I do not think Mother listened to what Mrs Boarder said. 'I'm getting him out of it. He's not staying there,' she said. This was marvellous. 'Yes,' she went on, 'before I go to work in the morning I'll be round to the Co-op to see if they'll take him on there.'

They would, as office boy in the General Offices and at almost three times my present wage.

'Ten shillings a week and a job for life!' Polly Mytton exclaimed. 'What a lucky lad he is.'

The pawnbroker put on an injured air when he heard my news. He inquired what my wages were to be and, when told, said: 'But *I* will give you ten shillings a week.'

Had I been a dutiful son I suppose I ought to have been

grateful for the good fortune that had come my way. Certainly it was an immense relief not to have to rise at dawn and go breakfastless to stand shivering on the pawnshop's step. Then again, there was the better pay—but I was exchanging one desk for another, and of these I already had had more than my fill. Moreover, the new job was defective in a most important particular; its early closing day, like that at the pawnshop, was Wednesday. Once more I would be odd man out, tied of a Saturday afternoon when all my friends were off enjoying themselves in a happy band.

Any loving mother, I felt, ought to be only too ready to save her son from this martyrdom. Besides, it wasn't as though I did not wish to pull my weight; on the contrary, I had a catalogue of jobs that would have brought me bliss on top of the necessary wages. Because of man-power shortages apprentices by the score were being taken on at Marlowe's Engineering; boys were wanted at the London and North Western Railway's engine sheds. There was carpentry, cabinet-making and my grandfather's craft. I begged, I pleaded, I cajoled: 'Please. Please. Any job where I can use my hands.'

In vain. In each of the trades I mentioned I was reminded of the ever-present spectres of short time, strikes and lock-outs. 'It is a clean job you've got and you'll wear a collar and tie. There's a week's holiday remember, *and* no short time. As for your gallivanting all over Manchester of a Saturday...' The sentence was left unfinished or, rather, it was finished with a look. 'Another thing, when we get the piano you'll be able to spend all Wednesday afternoon practising with nobody to interrupt. And not so much of the mumbling and grumbling, young man. Read what it says up there on the wall.' A finger pointed to the gilt frame on the wall. I did not need to read. The frame hung by the door; it had to be passed on every exit and entrance. The capitals were printed in gold, the lower case in red, the whole in what is known as

'Old English type'. 'Train up a child in the way he should go; and when he is old, he will not depart from it (Proverbs xxii, 6).' In case this was not enough Mother went to Grandfather's bookcase and, really giving me what-for, took out the Bible, opened the Holy Book at Proverbs xxix and read aloud, in all solemnity, 'The rod and reproof give wisdom: but a child left to himself bringeth his mother to shame.' She closed the book with a snap, concluding, 'And let me remind you, choirboy that you are, I have never had to raise my hand to either of you ... yet.'

Mutinously I went into the street where my contemporaries of both sexes were happily at play. A gang of lads was noisily engaged in a game of kick-can; my sister, sitting on a stool against the wall surrounded by a semicircle of little girls, was playing schoolmistress. Hetty Boarder, a man's battered straw hat tipped rakishly over one eye, had lifted her fraying skirt and was dancing the can-can to the music of Billy Seeley's accordion, Alfie supplying the rhythm with a couple of pairs of rib bones while Nobby did his best on a Jew's harp.

These happy frolics only served to distend my dolour so, to spite myself and to wallow in self-pity, I took a sulky mooch round the unrelieved desolation of the gasworks area. — And serve me right.

# 18

# Pills to Swallow

It was Wednesday. My sister had left for afternoon school. The streets were not yet empty. I could hear footfalls, clogged and booted, and snatches of conversation of people on their way back to workshop and mill. In a few minutes I would hear it, that note which for me had come to mean the voice of hopelessness and melancholy, the thin, high piping wail of the steam laundry's whistle. It prolonged itself after all the other blaring sirens and buzzers had stopped and, after it had died away, a forbidding lifelessness fell upon the streets. And I knew then that my hungry ears would be listening with fretful and brooding envy to the distant throb of Marlowe's Engineering works and the pulsing, muffled beat of its great drop-hammer. Or, again from the far, far distance might come the screeching whistle of a London and North Western Express. Sounds that mocked and jeered reminding me that I had been cheated of my heart's desire.

Dejectedly I saw myself filling in the empty hours of the afternoon traipsing the public park or sitting in the reading-room of the public library with old men, waiting my turn to look at the illustrated weeklies' photographs and drawings of the week's battles by land and sea.

A knock at the door. Hetty Boarder holding a small, flat, brown-paper parcel and a field service postcard from Flanders. She said: 'My mam says will you write it for her. Cigarettes for me dad. That's where you've to send it to— there, on the postcard.'

I asked her in and, as I wrote, I noticed out of the corner of my eye that she was making heel and toe movements on our hearth-rug while softly humming a tune. When I had

finished addressing the parcel she said: 'Do you like them?'
She lifted the hem of her skirts to her calves, raised her
right foot and waggled it. 'My *clogs*.' She emphasized the
word a little crossly at my want of understanding. She
smiled and was not successful when she tried to conceal her
pride. 'I won 'em at the Prince o' Wales matinee last
Saturday. Clog-dancing competition.' She let go her skirts
and, pouting, mumbled: 'But she won't let me go.'

'Who?'

'My mam.'

'Where?'

'On the stage, o' course.'

'Oh, yes,' I said, remembering. Poor Hetty. My heart
went out to her in sympathy at the hopeless incongruity of
her ambition.

Her sulky expression returned: 'She says I've got to stay
where I am in the steam laundry.'

'I know how you feel,' I said. 'Look at me, a blooming
office.' The stage-struck girl was not interested in my
problems. With a far-away expression she was off on wings
of fancy while I looked at her sagging, second-hand raincoat
that was a couple of sizes too big for her, at her shabby gone-
at-the-seams frock which she had outgrown: nor could I help
noticing how conspicuously she had developed in the right
places. I also noticed her lovely complexion, pale skin, pink
cheeks, curling eye-lashes and hair, like her mother's, black
as a raven. She came back to earth. Determinedly she said,
'But when me dad comes home on leave agen me Uncle
Fred's going to ask him for me. He's all right, me uncle is.
Let's me in back stage at the Prince o' Wales'. You can see
everything up in the flies.' She made a face. 'Some of those
girl dancers, though—. Poo. O' course, I'm not supposed to
be up there. But ... ' She slowly closed a large, dark eye and,
at that moment, there floated to our ears the starveling,
dismal lament of the steam laundry's whistle. 'Oh, lor!' she

cried, 'I'll have to scoot. Get murdered, I will, if I'm late.'
She flew. I heard the clop-clop of her running clogs fade
away.

Still, she knew what she wanted even though her desires,
like mine, were most unlikely ever to be realized.

Another knock on the front door, this time loud and
imperious. Irritably I went in answer. It was Nobby, uniformed and astride a red post-office bicycle. He had a foot
on our doorstep and he looked displeased.

'Where's Mrs Boarder?' he demanded. Ever since he had
donned telegraph lad's uniform he had become objectionably
cocky and even more so now that he was head boy. His voice
had broken and adolescent pimples adorned his face.

'How should I know?' I answered.

'Polly Mytton said that their Hetty was in here.' He gave
me a long, suspicious look, dismounted and entered.

'She's gone,' I said. 'Gone to work.'

'You want to watch that one,' he advised on a warning
note. 'Mind you,' he went on, 'I wouldn't mind havin' a
thrust.' With both hands he described hemispheres on his
chest. 'Real pair o' top 'uns she's got, hasn't she?' He then
gave me a nudge, grinned and took some postcard photographs from his inside pocket. 'Seen these?' He sniggered
and put the obscene pictures on the table. 'Look at that one.
Tell you, I'm goin' to have my share in them red lamps if
I'm pulled in the army. Coo! There's tail by the yard out
there.' He became businesslike and made a palm-upward
pass over the cards. 'Wanna buy any? Only chargin' ninepence each.' He shrugged when I declined, swept the
merchandise into his pocket, producing, from another, a dog-
eared pack of playing cards which, while speaking, he began
to shuffle expertly: 'What about it, then? Five minutes.
Pontoon?' He frowned. 'Oh, aye. Forgot. You don't gamble.'
Although this was a fact there wasn't any virtue in it for me
where Nobby was concerned. Mickmac and others who had

fallen victim to Nobby's manipulative skill had come to the
conclusion that Nobby's luck was too consistent to be true.
'Oh, well,' he said and put the cards away. He delved into
his inside breast pocket and, winking, took out a thick wad
of other cards rounded at their edges. These were scented
and, on their front, bore a picture of an Oriental dancing
girl wearing a yashmak. 'Here y'are. I'm chargin' sixpence
a dozen. Penny each they're marked. You could sell dozens
to those girls in that office o' yours.' He turned a card over.
The printing read: 'In aid of the Wounded Soldiers' Fund.'

'Where did you get these from?'

'Mind your own business,' he answered, resentfully.
'D'you want any, that's the point. Easy money, remember.'
He shrugged when I declined. 'Okay. Suit yourself.' His
frown deepened. 'And I've not got all day to waste muckin'
about waiting for Ma Boarder. Look at this lot.' He un-
fastened the pouch on his belt and took out a wad of telegrams. 'Comin' in by the dozen, they are. Bert Harrington's
killed, y'know.' I stared. 'An' Reggie Niblo. He's gone. So is
Dick Dacre and Alfie's dad. Just given the telegram to Polly
Mytton for him. This Big Push, y'know. That's what it is.'
He interrupted himself. 'Hey, tell you what: *you* give it to
Ma Boarder. I'm not supposed to, but ... Oh, well, *you*
know.' He pushed the telegram into my hand, got on to his
bike and pedalled away.

Polly Mytton was on her doorstep talking to a neighbour.
She was holding the telegram for Alfie in her right hand, its
envelope in her left. Their subdued conversation ended as
Mrs Boarder turned the corner. Mrs Boarder had thrown the
cowl of her shawl on to her shoulders and I noticed that she
was not wearing her Spanish comb. Loaves stuck out of the
bag she carried in her right hand; her left gripped the
gathered hem of her sacking apron which bulged with
vegetables.

When she saw the telegram I was holding out to her she

said, 'Oh.' Then she added, 'Read out what it says, lad, my hands are full.' I obeyed. She made a little cough and said: 'Just put it in the bag, lad.' I did and she went into her house without another word.

Polly Mytton called me across. 'Who was it, lad, Harry or his dad?' She had put her hand to her mouth.

'Mr Boarder,' I said.

A fortnight later Nobby was round again at Mrs Boarder's. She said, dismayed, when he handed her the telegram, 'Nay, nay. Not our Harry as well.'

# 19

# Heart Throb

'The way it's going it'll be nought but a world o' widows,' Mrs Boarder said. She was sitting in our kitchen swaying to and fro as she patted her baby's back. Polly Mytton was at the table with my mother who had just returned from work with 'the bag'.

'Just look at that,' Polly said, indicating the newspaper Mother had brought home. It carried a gallery of photographs of men in uniform: below were the ghastly columns headed: 'Killed, Wounded and Missing.'

My mother shook her head. 'Sinful,' she said. 'Three years and more and the end no nearer.'

'And all for what?' Mrs Boarder went on, bitterly. 'Our Harry and his dad. Gone. What for? That's what I ask myself many and many a time when I think o' the millions the profiteers're making out of the slaughter. Then I think back an' I ask myself what have any of us had out o' life.' She nodded towards our bookcase: 'Talk about your dad's books, lass, I've a collection of my own. There's the rent book, the tick book, weekly payment book, ration book, what-I-owe-the-soddin'-doctor book and the burial club book, lapsed and all the years o' payin' in down the drain. My God! If I could turn the clock back ... But they've gone, my two, so what's the use o' talk?'

Polly Mytton sighed and passed her palm over her snowy hair: 'It's this conscription,' she said, with a troubled look. 'He doesn't understand. He's still three years to go before he finishes his apprenticeship. Eighteen he'll be in a month or two's time and they've passed him and Nobby Clark A1 at the medical. I've come to look on that lad as my own son. I love him. He's such good company.'

Alfie. After his father had gone off to the war Polly had taken him into her home. Marvelling, he had told us of his new life. 'Clean sheets and blankets on my bed! She gives me a breakfast *every* mornin' and there's allus summat ready for me to eat after work. Makes me say my prayers, she does. And when she's in her bed and I'm in mine we sing "Lord keep us safe this night, secure from all our fears." Then we say "Good night. God bless." Tell you. I can't get over it.'

Mother looked at Polly, regarding her with incredulity: 'Alfie? Eighteen? Eighteen, did you say? He looks no more than a lad just left school.'

'It's his size,' Mrs Boarder said. 'Poor little devil. And can you wonder, having to fend for himself like a waif.'

Mother couldn't get over it. 'But him — ! A soldier!'

'There it is,' Polly said, shaking her head. 'It's a new regiment he says they're starting. "The Bantams" they're calling it. All of 'em little men.'

'It's like I've said already,' Mrs Boarder repeated. 'Before it's done there won't be a man left. And —,' she interrupted herself as the baby began to cough. 'There, there, love,' she said, adding, 'Can't seem to rid him of it, poor little feller. Spit and image of his dad and there was me saying I didn't want him.'

Polly recommended blackcurrant tea; Mother said that goose-grease was the thing: ' ... that's what my mother was never without for chest complaints: said it'll penetrate a stone.' She began to dish out the contents of the bag. 'It's getting worse and worse now the rationing's been brought in. The cook doesn't know which way to turn.'

'She's not alone,' Mrs Boarder said, adding, to the baby, 'Cough it up, lad. *There* it is. And it'll be blackcurrant tea and goose-grease for thee and a scutch across the chops for our Hetty if I have much more of it from her.'

'Something wrong, Annie?' Mother asked.

'Stage, stage, stage, at me morning, noon and night and

her with a good job at the steam laundry. I don't know what
the young 'uns 're coming to these days. But what can you
expect—no father around. Ay, *I* don't know.'

There was another thing she did not know. Alfie had
confessed to me his helpless, hopeless love for Hetty and his
dread of her going on to the stage and out of his life.

'What does she say?' I asked him. He looked at me,
puzzled. I went on: 'Haven't you asked her?'

'Oh, no,' he glanced at me quickly as though this were
the last thing in his mind. Thinking to console him I
ridiculed Hetty's ambition. He astonished me by rising
indignantly to her defence as though I had offered his idol
an unforgivable insult, but he was placated to some extent
when I lyingly assured him that I did not mean it the way
he had chosen to take it.

'I know she'll go,' he mumbled, miserably. 'I can feel it.
An'—you know—I don't like to ask her if she'd wait for me
till I come back out o' the army.' He fetched a shuddering
sigh. 'Yes, she'll go, all right. You'll see.'

None of us saw her go. Some weeks later her mother, now
reconciled, excitedly announced that the company of which
Hetty was now a member was booked to appear at the
Regent Theatre. It was a mixed bill headed by a top-line
comedian and a star vocalist. Hetty was one of the troupe
of 'Klancy's Komedy Kids'.

We—Nobby, Alfie, Mickmac and I—were down the side
alley in the queue known as 'the tuppenny rush'. The
commissionaire-cum-chucker-out paced up and down the
theatre frontage bawling 'Early doors this way!' Galleryites,
prepared to fork out the extra penny, preceded us and had
the pick of the seats. Five minutes or so before 'Overture and
beginners' was called the commissionaire stalked to the
gallery pay-box and said, 'Let 'em in,' at which there was a
general stampede up the interminable stone steps to 'the
gods'.

So far as Alfie was concerned the top-line comedian, the star vocalist and other attractions on the bill were non-existent. When Klancy's Komedy Kids came on, not only he but Nobby, Mickmac and I were utterly staggered. For years Hetty had bamboozled us under the masquerade of a shabby, unconsidered street tomboy playing hopscotch and joining in our games. The girl who now hypnotized our marvelling eyes never could have had identity with us and back streets. There she was, conspicuous in her superb and radiant vitality, leading the troupe with effortless ease and the confident felicity of 'a natural'. As finale and on a cue from the band, she danced to the prompt corner, took a swagger cane and a soldier's peaked cap, danced back to stage centre where, taking the spotlight, with the rest of the troupe marking time behind her, she began to sing, with winks and thigh slappings:

'Serjeant Brown, Serjeant Brown, keep your eye on
                                        Tommy for me,
For he might go wrong on the continong when he lands
                                        in Gay Paree.
Parley voo as they always do when a French girl they
                                        see,
But if my boy Tommy wants to parley voo, let him
                                        come home and parley voo
                                        with me.'

After the show Nobby, hungry for fish and chips, refused to wait to see the company emerge. He went off with Mickmac. 'I'm glad he's gone,' Alfie said and began to saunter away from the passage which led to the stage door.

'Where are you going?' I asked, puzzled.

'Come on,' he answered, 'I'll treat you to an ice-cream,' and I followed him into the marbled and mirrored splendour of an Italian's establishment next the theatre's main entrance. I was no stranger to this place nor had I told anybody that

I had lost my heart to the proprietor's daughter. She was the incarnation of Lord Leighton's portrait of 'The Captive Andromache'. Her eyes were big, dark and sorrowing, her hair was raven, and large gold rings hung from her ears. She seemed always to be staring, over my head unfortunately, as though on the look-out for the approach of a lover. Many a time I had spent my all sitting at one of the marble-topped tables sighing heavily as I stared and licked my ice-cream, but those beautiful, haunting eyes were quite blind to my dog-like devotion.

I noticed that Andromache was not in attendance. Alfie gave her father the order and we watched him delve into the freezer and scoop out a couple of dollops. We took these to a table by the window where, again, I was puzzled when Alfie insisted on sitting with his back to it while I faced him playing the look-out.

'I don't want her to see me,' he explained. 'You see,' he went on, hesitantly, 'it was Reggie Sniblo she liked. She never told him but she told me. He wanted to go on the stage, too. Did you know?' He cannot have heard my answer since I had scarcely uttered the first word before he was expressing his agony in a stifled groan. '*You* don't know what it's like to feel the way I do.' He paused, looked at me with eyes full of pleading: 'Will *you* write?'

'Who to?'

'Hetty, o' course. But don't say it's for me. Just a ... just ask her for a photo to take with me when I'm called up.'

Klancy's Komedy Kids came chattering past the window under the fussy care of their matron. 'There she is,' I said.

He strained round. When the troupe had passed he rose and I did likewise. I did not remind him that he had not touched his ice-cream.

His call-up papers arrived soon afterwards and we all turned out to watch the parade from the barracks to the train. The barracks doors opened and out marched the

latest conscripts in their civvies, the lack of inches of 'the
Bantams' made more conspicuous by Nobby and his group
bringing up the rear. Away they went, preceded by the
blaring band, past shawled mothers with long faces
crowding the pavements.

I was standing with Polly Mytton, her silver hair blowing
about, tears running down her apple cheeks. She raised her
hand as Alfie, grinning, marched by: 'Keep yourself well
wrapped up, lad,' she called. 'Ay,' she went on to the
women around, 'Bless 'em. Look at 'em all. They're nowt
but children.'

# 20

# Somebody Else Discontented

There was the other war, the one within myself. In this the possibility of a truce was out of the question. The racking turmoil would have been more endurable had I known what would have satisfied that demanding and perpetually discontented other self. All that I was certain of was that imprisonment in an office for the rest of my days would be insufferable and that, as the suppressed pressures intensified with the passing months, the volcano, sooner or later, would erupt.

The Co-operative Society's offices were crowned with a louvred tower capped with a dome which had a small room below approached by a narrow flight of dusty stairs. It was a forgotten place, a graveyard for discarded books of accounts, hundreds of thick leather-bound ledgers thrown in anyhow for mites to feed on. I was its only regular visitor and, to its dusty chaos, had brought a semblance of order by stacking the discarded ledgers into a rough-and-ready Jacob's ladder from whose summit I sat and peered through the louvres at clouds drifting in the free ranges of the sky.

Here my mutinous *alter ego* kicked off all shackles and burst forth to run free and wild like a colt turned loose in the fields of May. But not for long. My twin selves reunited to return, grudgingly, to the abomination of the high stool and desk. One thing was certain, I consoled myself: by fair means or foul I would break free of them for ever, how and when I did not know.

There was the other balm when servitude at the desk became intolerable: remembrances of all the wonderful music with which, increasingly, I was becoming on familiar terms.

Thanks to the private enterprise of Sir Thomas Beecham and the frequent complimentary tickets that came my mother's way there was not an opera, Russian, German, French or Italian, we had not heard. To this heady brew, when funds would run to it, we had the additional intoxication of the Hallé concerts at the Free Trade Hall every Thursday. It was at one of these concerts that, to my astonishment, I found myself envied.

This particular concert was devoted to the works of Bach, Mozart, Beethoven and Wagner. During the interval we amateur critics who were priggish and self-opinionated left our seats to form small groups in the Hall's corridors where we aired our knowledge and held forth, sometimes adversely, on the solo performances of instrumental celebrities of international reputation. For me, the most aggravating members of our carping fraternity were those few who called attention to themselves by bringing with them the full score of whatever principal item was on the programme. With this open on their knees during the performance they frowned, tut-tutted and shook their heads as, with restrained gestures, they conducted the performance in competition with the professional on the rostrum. In the world of literature they have their entertaining counterparts who like to criticize a writer's work with pencilled marginal comments such as 'Bosh', 'The man's mad', 'Utterly ridiculous' etc.

On this occasion, during an interval, one such, with thick spectacles, a black floppy bow tie and long, frizzy, receding hair, was poking his forefinger at the score while vehemently holding forth on something in the performance that had displeased him.

I caught the eye of a young man at my side. He said: 'That kind give me the pip.' He was pale, hollow-cheeked, inclined to be stoop-shouldered: there was fire in his eyes. We moved away from the vehement critic. I began to enthuse over the Siegfried Idyll which had concluded the

programme's first half. We fell into conversation; then, his
eyes glowing, he indicated the programme's four composers
with whose countries we were at war: ' ... and can you
believe it, there are patriotic idiots in this country who call it
"enemy" music and want to have it banned. Barbarians!
Why, if it hadn't been for the German community here we
never would have had the Hallé Orchestra.' He went on to
denounce the war passionately, concluding; 'I wouldn't have
gone even if I weren't C 3. I'm a conscientious objector and
I don't care who knows it. No, I wouldn't go. I'd take prison
first,' He paused for breath, eyes still glowing. 'Do you live
here? Manchester, I mean?' He nodded when I told him:
'Salford. Same thing.' He fetched an envious sigh, then
mentioned the village where he lived, twenty miles or so
away, buried in the heart of the Pennines. 'Aren't you
lucky.'

'Lucky?' I answered, puzzled. 'I wish I lived in the
country.'

'Yes,' he murmured thoughtfully on a low note, then he
glanced at me, quickly. 'I'd change places with you any time.
Look—' he pulled the *Manchester Guardian* from his pocket: it
was open at the theatre advertisements page. 'Quay Street,
Peter Street, Oxford Street—' The Free Trade Hall is in the
centre of these contiguous streets. He began to tap the
advertisement columns. 'Eight theatres in three streets, all
number one dates—all on your doorstep. I don't think you
realize just what you've got.' The fire died from his eyes
and was replaced by a hungry suppliance. 'What I'd give
to live here. Once a month, that's the only time I can get
away. Have to leave fifteen minutes before the concert's
end to catch the last train. Purgatory. I tell you, you don't
know how lucky you are. Where do you work?'

I told him and added, 'But I'm not going to stay there.'

'What are you planning to do?'

'I don't know. But it won't be an office.'

'I know what I'm going to do,' he said, with emphasis. ' ... I mean when the war's over. Stuck where I am for the duration. But the minute I'm free ... ' His eyes glowed again. 'I'll be here in Manchester and I'll find a job. I'll do anything. Anything, and I shan't care what it is.'

Our eyes met. Simultaneously and without benefit of words we both saw the funny side of it and we laughed.

There was a drifting back to the hall. He turned a page of the programme to the concert's second part. 'Beethoven and Mozart,' he said, with zest, put his head on one side, clicked his tongue and winked as we went to our seats.

# 21

# *What Next?*

Bonfires in the streets: pubs crowded to the doors. At eleven o'clock throughout the land that November morning the air danced with the joyous clangour of church bells which, in our parts, were lost in the prolonged blasts from mill and factory hooters and the deeper notes of ships' sirens in the Salford docks. Mill and factory hands, shop and office workers downed tools and pens and, without a by-your-leave to anybody, poured cheering into the streets and made holiday to celebrate the end of the war to end wars.

Here and there in the industrial areas to which the victorious troops returned there rose a new institution — hastily assembled army huts and converted derelict Reformatory Schools to cope with floods of workless soldiers and others waiting for industry to gear itself to the pursuits of peace. 'Employment Bureau' it said on the boards above the entrances. Immediately the places were dubbed 'the burroo' and the weekly benefits paid to those who 'signed on' became known universally as 'the dole'. But all this was a matter of small moment. The killing was over, army gratuities jingled in pockets and men waiting for jobs did not mind a spell of leisure in which to enjoy the general restlessness of the times.

My own restlessness was at flash point. The route from home to office had become a Via Dolorosa, and in this safe job which was mine for life I saw myself imprisoned for the rest of my days, like one of the skylarks the local miners kept in tiny string-topped cages. And there was Hetty Boarder's fine example for ever nagging me. She had triumphed over all maternal threats and had shaken off her chains. And what

of Nobby and Alfie? Warriors baptized in fire and now with
the Army of Occupation and billeted, my nagging envy
reminded me, in Bonn, where Beethoven was born.

Ledgers, ledgers, ledgers. The staring regiment of them
mocked my impotence. Of the whole boiling only one had
interest for me, and in letters of gold on its spine were the
words STUD BOOK. Within were the names and particulars
of every horse owned by the Co-op. My heart was with all
that this stood for, the out o' doors and, preferably, miles
from Salford where fields were green and where, if you put
your hand on a tree trunk, your palm was not sullied by soot.
Oh, dreams, dreams.

My mother received a letter from the Society's secretary.
Would she please call to see him. In the privacy of his office
with stern, maternal eyes upon me I was carpeted. On the
secretary's desk were a number of account books and
registers of the Society's membership each open at pages
which I had decorated with pencil drawings of horses. It
was my own fault. They ought to have been erased.

I came in for another ticking off at home. 'Do you not
understand ... ' etc. Luckily the admonition was interrupted
by a visit from Mrs Boarder and Polly Mytton: 'We thought
you'd like to give a copper or two, lass,' Mrs Boarder said:
'A whip-round we're having. All the lads that joined up.
We're having their names wrote out on a Roll of Honour and
put in a case on the wall in Rossall Street. A memorial, like.'

Polly Mytton, who looked pleased at what she had to say,
added: 'The vicar's coming. Holding a bit of a service in the
street. And we're having a little shelf put under the case for
flowers.'

Mother paid up.

'And,' Mrs Boarder said, with a straight face, 'if you've
any other money lying around that you want to invest, go
and see old Wheelam. He'll make your fortune for you—so
he says.' Since the death of his sister and his retirement from

the mill Mrs Boarder was doing his chores. 'You can both stare,' Mrs Boarder assured Polly and my mother. 'Sold all his property, he told me, and every penny piece he's got he's put into cotton mill shares. Off to Oldham twice a week, he is. Stock Exchange, or something, he says. His money's doubled already. Reckons that in another year he'll be able to sell out for fifty thousand pounds, then he's off to Bournemouth and live like a lord.'

'Well, I never ... !' Polly said, impressed.

'Got rid of his pipe,' Mrs Boarder went on. 'Oh, yes. Nothing so common. Cigars, now. And the way he's going it won't be long before he's got one in his mouth and a couple more stickin' out o' both ears.' She shook her head. 'Have *I* any money to invest, he says. Silly old devil. Haven't got sixpence to scrat my arse with.' Her glance fell on me. 'And what's up with him, down in the dumps. Anything wrong?'

Comfortingly, Polly Mytton smiled at me when Mother had revealed the cause. 'It's his age,' she said. 'He'll grow out of it.'

'I had just the same problem with our Hetty,' Mrs Boarder declared. 'It's like I've always said. It's what comes of not having a father behind 'em.'

I loved Polly when she laughed and said, 'Get on with you, Annie Boarder. It's youth. I was a real madam when I was his age. As for you and your fathers—little Alfie had one and the innocent mite was afraid for his life. Thank God no harm befell him and he'll be home again. Aye, and still got three years of his apprenticeship to serve. It was a crime taking him, that it was.'

'It's his future I'm thinking of ... Job for life ... If only I knew what he wanted to do.' Mother's anxious expression and her words filled me with self-condemnation and angry self-justification at one and the same time.

'Spread his wings,' Polly said, 'that's what he wants to do, so why don't you let him? We're only young once.'

5

'If only I knew what he wanted to do.' There was no question of my knowing what I wanted to do; the desire for this was consuming.

Falling away steeply near our parish church is Brindle-heath Road and, at its foot, railway sidings. At every meeting of Manchester races the horse-boxes were shunted here. Whenever I could I haunted this place to watch the aristocrats of the equine world being unloaded. There they were, hooded and sheeted in richly coloured and monogrammed rugs, knee-capped and ankle-booted, proud creatures of a high, remote and exciting world, a world redolent of green fields and gallops where the winds sang. There they were, elegant, refined, light-footed and conspicuously incongruous as they traversed the back streets of Salford. And my yearning, hungry heart burned with envy and respect for the dapper pygmies who sat their nervous charges as these pranced, bucked and reared at all the unnatural clangours and startling sights common to the town.

But how was this ambition to be accomplished? I hadn't the remotest connection with anybody in the racing game and, what was worse, had never been astride anything on four legs. I was reaching for the moon. Inconsequently I remembered my mother's customary rebuke when, muttering impatiently, I went about the house looking for something I could not find. 'Under your nose, young man, like everything else you'll be looking for in this life.' Here, unhappily, was one occasion when the truth of this wisdom did not apply. Though ...

One of my jobs in the office was the responsibility for the outgoing post, the recording of every charge and the purchase of the necessary stamps. Twice daily, morning and afternoon, I had the pleasure of walking to the post office and wasting as much time as I dared on the way back.

Of late, around nine thirty mark, I had noticed with intense pleasure and respectful curiosity the anachronistic appearance of two horsemen: a grey-bearded gentleman with the air of a Cavalier trailed by a bowler-hatted groom. The gentleman's mount was a docile grey mare, the groom's a bay gelding. The ride ended at the parish church where the gentleman dismounted, got into a four-wheel cab and was driven away in the direction of Manchester.

Who was the gentleman and where did he live? Inquiry revealed him to be a cotton spinner and manufacturer, his place of residence Swinton, three miles or so distant.

One evening, without preliminary, I presented myself presumptuously at the front door of his imposing residence, rang the bell and asked the maid if I might see him. She told me to wait and, returning presently, invited me in. I was received by the gentleman, who listened courteously to my inquiry as to the possibility of my being employed in his stables. I was interrogated closely and, to my gratification, was asked to bring a testimonial as to character from the vicar of our parish. This was delivered without delay and, to my great joy, I was engaged.

When I brought the glad news to my mother she gave me a long look, sighed, shook her head and said: 'What next?'

# 22

# *Heart's Desire*

It was a big house with lawns and flower gardens enclosed by a high wall and it stood in Swinton Park. In Victoria's reign the Park had been an exclusive area of large residences, all with spacious walled gardens, coach house and stables. There were one or two farms and a golf links. A broad, tree-lined unmade road ran the Park's length and, on this, one or two of the residences stood derelict. Empty and unwanted, they had been used during the war as emergency housing for Belgian refugee families.

The high iron gates at the road's head were kept open permanently now. Courting couples ignored the peeling notice PRIVATE ROAD on the brick gate-posts and, in the dusk and darkness, couched in the fields and told the old sweet tale.

My employer maintained four riding horses and an old-age pensioner, a hackney called Charlie who, in his younger days and as leader in a tandem team, had carried off the red ribbon at the Dublin Horse Show. The carriage horses were gone, though their harness decorated the glass-fronted case in the saddle and tack room. What had been the coach-house now housed a Daimler limousine and a sports car, both in the loving care of the head chauffeur who, as a profitable side-line, traded occasionally in second-hand motor bikes. I learned that his wife had disappeared with a lover, though this calamity did not seem to bother him in the slightest degree for he was always singing merrily, his favourite song being:

> Everything is peaches down in Georgia,
> What a peach of a day, for a wedding in May ...

The second chauffeur, of jockey size, wore breeches and leggings, had a fresh complexion and walked briskly with quick short steps. Previous to my coming he had helped exercise the horses. He was afflicted with a stammer and was a lady-killer, in proof of which he had a collection of postcard photographs of his conquests, dog-eared from his boastful habit of showing them to everybody.

I had been left in his charge whilst the groom rode the bay and the grey on a leg stretch before taking them up to the house. He waved a hand towards a dung fork: 'Muck 'em out,' he said and nodded to the first stall occupied by a mare of seventeen hands. He grinned, winked at me and walked to the animal's side. It put its ears back, showed the whites of its eyes and began to toss its head. He then ran his palm under her belly, crying at the same time and in jocular tones, 'Ah-raaah, come on, then. Let's feel your little titties.' This he did while the mare, resenting the liberty, tried to hook him with vicious forward kicks of her near-side hind leg and, at the same time, she began a savage biting of the manger. He stopped and laughed. 'Gets it every morning, she does.' He added, as though I stood in doubt about the matter, 'She doesn't like it.' He came out of the stall. 'Daisy's her name. And you watch her.' There was warning in his tones. 'I tell you. The mounted police couldn't do anything with her. Threw her out.' He pointed to a wall-eyed, cow-hocked Arab grey three stalls away. 'Sisyphus, that one. What a name. Daft as they come. Him at the top, that's Charlie. Could do with the clippers but the guv'nor won't have him touched. Those other two that're out, they're Prince and Maggie. Maggie's the grey, Mr Tom's charger in the war. She won a medal, y'know. Wounded in battle. Take a squint at her right flank, you'll see the mark.' He lit a cigarette and regarded me quizzically: 'You've not been with horses before, have you?' I told him that I had not and, in answer to his further questioning, confessed my previous employment. He looked at me amazed. 'Giving that up for this?' he said, incredulously; then he tapped his temple and with his forefinger made an ascending spiral movement. 'O' course, you're doo-lally; must *like* punishment.' He spat. I could feel it coming, the condescending assumption that any values other than his own were futile: with mounting irritation I asked myself what could he know about the torture of imprisonment in offices. But I held my tongue. 'Love a duck, man, it's a seven days a week job, is hosses. Why d'you think I went in for the cars?' He inclined his head towards the saddle-room. 'He's cottoned on. I'm giving him driving lessons.' He started to stroll away, then paused in the doorway: 'Take my tip—learn to drive. An' if you want a winner—Oranmore in the two thirty. A dead cert.' He departed whistling.

As I was heaving the last basket of muck on to the midden a man came through the stable archway pushing a barrow. He wore heavy boots, a cap and a green baize apron under his jacket. He stopped by the midden, looked at it, took the clay pipe from his mouth and pointed its stem at my heaped handiwork. 'That won't do,' he said. 'You don't leave it like that—ought to have more sense. Spread it even. Understand? Don't you think I've enough to do what with the garden an' the lawns and them in there?' His hand holding the pipe swung to the upper end of the stable block. Recognizing his voice, 'them in there' set up a low mooing. 'Right, then,' he said. 'Get it straightened,' and he trundled the barrow to the cow-house.

The groom did not look at all pleased when, returning, he saw how I was employed. Dismounting he called me to him and required to know who had set me working on the midden. 'I might ha' known' he said, loudly, when I told him. He addressed the words to the cow-house door. Still loudly, he said to me: 'You take your orders from me and nobody else. That understood? And that goes for anybody and everybody in this here yard.' We led Maggie and Prince into the stable. 'Unsaddle 'em and rug 'em up,' he said, then walked to Maggie's manger and glanced into the water compartment. 'And keep these filled.' He then jerked his thumb at the hay cratches. 'These too. Kettle on? Then put it on and brew up. Put the saddles on the saddle-horse next door and I'll show you how a saddle *ought* to be cleaned when I've had my char.'

He was sitting drinking tea, smoking a second cigarette and reading the second chauffeur's *Sporting Chronicle* by the time I had fulfilled his commands. 'Right,' he said, putting the newspaper aside. 'Groomin'. There's the gear, in that bucket. Take the brushes out, leave the sponge in, fill it full o' water and purra jerk in it.' He was in his shirtsleeves when he came into the stable. 'Right,' he said, standing behind Daisy. 'This is how you start. The sponge. Jump to it. Pass us the sponge. Come on.' I followed him to the mare's head. He wiped her eyes. 'Eyes,' he said, then her nostrils. 'Nose,' he said and moved to her hindquarters. He dropped the sponge into the bucket, took it out dripping, lifted the mare's tail and sloshed it on to her privy parts. ' ... and dock,' he said, recapitulating: 'Eyes, nose and dock. Get it? Right. Now. Groomin'. Can you ride? Oh, I see. Well, better get you started when I've a minute.'

This was an unconscionable time a-coming. Any spare time that came the groom's way was spent taking instruction on the mysteries of the internal combustion engine. However, with an eye on acquitting myself in decent fashion at my first attempt in the saddle, I spent each evening at the Public Reference Library devouring an illustrated article on 'Riding' in the *Encyclopaedia Britannica*. Full instructions in all branches of equitation were given but, in the whole of its length, the piece was silent on the great gulf that exists between theory and practice. I was not to be left in ignorance of this for long.

Because of a cutting January wind that blustered in from the north-east, a message came from the house that this morning the guv'nor had decided against his customary ride. 'Okay,' the groom said to me, 'Daisy needs exercisin'. Now's your chance.' He gave me a saddle and a double bridle, adding, as an afterthought, 'Better have her on a leadin' rein. She'll be a bit fresh after standing in.'

Unbeknown to the groom or anybody else I had been astride Daisy on several occasions. These had taken place when the yard staff had gone to their midday meal and I, to get the feel of things, had put a saddle on Daisy while she was tethered in her stall. She had stood there staring with indifference at the wall. I also had nursed the hope that, when my lessons began, these would have been progressive, beginning, say, on the back of Charlie who wasn't even shod now out of respect for his age, then graduating via the docile Maggie, whose manners were impeccable as became a lady to whom battle honours had been awarded and who, also, was the mount of an elderly gentleman.

'Better have her on a leading rein. She'll be a bit fresh after standing in.' The words repeated themselves to my apprehensive mind as the groom, having mounted Prince, took hold of Daisy's leading rein and said: 'Up you go, then.' Up I clumsily went and, before I had my right foot in the stirrup, Daisy had gone into a most vigorous tap-dancing routine which immediately reduced me to a state of agitated jellification.

'Put your elbows in. Heels down, there. Grip with your knees.' The groom barked out the orders serjeant-major fashion, then, as we passed under the stable arch, the quiet air was riven by the hideous explosive racket of the unseen sports car's engine.

Daisy reared, whipped round and ran backwards, a movement which, any skilled horseman will confirm, is the most difficult to manage since it has the effect of pitching him

forward perpetually—as I was with my arms embracing
Daisy's neck as though I were her passionate lover. The
groom sent Prince forward, unceremoniously shoved Daisy's
head round, told me to get back into the saddle and asked
me what did I think reins and bits were for. I could not
answer since the equine ballet my mount was performing
was jouncing all the breath from my body. 'Look,' the groom
said, not taking the slightest notice of my discomfort. 'Look,'
he said, making a double loop of his reins, placing them
across Prince's chine and leaning the whole of his weight on
it. 'That's the drill when you're thrown forward. Common
sense. Get hold of her.' He shortened his reins. 'We'll try the
trot.' Privately I wondered what he thought Daisy had been
doing ever since leaving the stable yard. The moment I
shortened rein Daisy plunged forward. 'Not the canter, man.
Hold her in.' We fell into a fast trot. My mentor then said,
reprovingly: 'Rise in the saddle. You're not in the Household
Cavalry. *Rise*, like me.' He was rising and falling with
graceful rhythm, missing a beat, as it were. My efforts to
follow suit were frustrated by Daisy's unpredictable gymnastics. After sixty minutes or so of this and despite the cutting
wind I was in a muck-sweat, dizzy, filleted, and wishing the
writer of the *Encyclopaedia Britannica*'s article would spend the
same amount of time astride Daisy then retire instantly to
his desk to revise his piece. However, by the time the hour
was up and though I could not say that I was in control, at
least I still was in the saddle; moreover, when Daisy decided
to fall into a clumsy trot I found myself occasionally
imitating my companion's expert rise and fall.

Behind us we heard the 'parp-parp' of the Daimler's bulb
horn. 'Left wheel,' the groom commanded. 'Swing her
round,' and used his mount to nudge Daisy to stand at right
angles. He brought up a smart military salute as the guv'nor
went by then ticked me off for not having followed suit. As
we resumed our way, watching the Daimler disappear in the

dusty distance, he said: 'There he goes. The last of 'em.' He shook his head and sighed, heavily: 'Aye, you can say that you're riding the last of the saddle horses that'll ever be seen in these parts.' He threw me a glance. 'That's why I'm learning all about motors. Won't be long before the guv'nor retires — then what? I'll be looking for a job.' He shrugged: 'Oh, well, there it is. Way of the world.'

We came to the Park's gates. 'Right,' he said. 'You're getting the hang of it. Let's see how you shape on your own.' He reached forward to Daisy's bridle to slip the leading rein. 'Get a hold of her. Show her who's master.'

At the precise moment Daisy was free a Foden steam waggon on the near-by Bolton Road relieved itself of excessive boiler pressure in an ear-splitting, house-shaking prolonged hiss that set even the phlegmatic sparrows in panic-stricken flight. Daisy reared, wheeled, showed her backside to Prince, to Foden's steam waggon, the grinding tramcars and all the other alarming noises on the King's highway and, with me being helplessly jogged, bounced and jarred, bolted at the gallop for home.

# 23

# Something in the System

Being at that time what is now known as 'a teenager'—I was,
I think, in my twentieth year—I had my share of the conceit
appropriate to that age. But my accomplishments in the
horse-riding line, such as they were, did not make the
slightest impression on any of my friends. Indeed they were
of the same opinion as the second chauffeur and thought it
eccentric of me to have chosen a job which was in the act of
being engulfed and extinguished in a permanent cloud of
stinking motor exhaust.

Still, there was my sister who was impressionable and my
mother who, by now, was reconciled.

Polly Mytton, having seen me riding Sisyphus when she
had been herb-gathering in Swinton Park, had mentioned
the fact to my mother. Foolishly I said: 'Oh, *him*. Anybody
could ride that one.'

'Not so much of the bragging, young man,' Mother said,
reprovingly. 'Remember "Pride goeth before a fall". You
watch out that Sisyphus doesn't throw you off.'

'Sisyphus?' I scoffed. 'Throw me? Not likely. And what
a daft name for a horse.'

'Daft?' I was surprised by the sharpness of her tone.

'Well. Sisyphus. It *is* daft. It doesn't mean anything.'

I knew that I had put my foot in it the instant I received
the shut-eye look of disdain which was reserved for exhibitions
of ignorance or bad manners.

Without a word Mother rose and crossed to Grandfather's
glass-fronted bookcase and took out *A Smaller Classical
Dictionary* whose fly-leaf was marked '6d', as were several of
the books which she was in the habit of bringing home. Of

late my sister and I had been hearing a lot about one of my mother's regular customers at the café, a professor at Manchester University. It was on his advice that she selected many of the titles from the threepenny and sixpenny shelves at the secondhand booksellers.

She opened the book at the proper page, placed it on the table in front of me, sat down and said: 'Proceed,' adding, with a quotation from the Collect for the Second Sunday in Advent, 'Read, mark, learn and inwardly digest.' I had scarcely read half a dozen words to myself when I heard: 'And read aloud.'

' "Sisyphus," ' I read. ' "Son of Aeolus, whence he is called Aeolides. He was married to Merope ... " ' I broke off and glanced at her. 'Do you want me to read it all?'

'All.'

I resumed, concluding: ' "His wickedness during life was severely punished in the lower world, where he had to roll uphill a huge marble block which as soon as it reached the top always rolled down again." Homer, *Odyssey*, XI, 593.'

'Remember, then, what happened to Sisyphus and mend your self-willed ways, gallivanting the streets when you could be improving your mind.' She pointed to the bookcase. 'Homer is in there. You don't need money to be well off. Times without number I've told you. Get the habit of reading and you will have a companion for life.'

I was grateful for the arrival of Polly Mytton who held an open letter. 'Hello, hello,' she said, 'is he copping it again?' She listened to what my mother had to say, laughed and won my love afresh when she said, 'Oh, leave him be. You can't put an old head on young shoulders.' She waved the letter. 'Look! Just come from Alfie, bless him. He gets his discharge three months from now. Ay, I will be glad to have him home. Three months from now, just at the start of spring.'

Daffodils in bud in sheltered spots of the guv'nor's garden, lambs'-tails in the hedges and, for me, a bursting restlessness.

When chauffeurs, groom and gardener had gone for their midday meal, I was alone in the saddle-room looking at the *Sporting Chronicle*'s photographs and reports of the coming Lincolnshire Handicap and Grand National. I got the whiff of gallops and the green fields far, far away. By way of reminder as to how far away they really were there came to my ears the dismal, distant piping of factory sirens and their melancholy message of mills and mean streets.

My eyes fell on a two-line advertisement under the Situations Vacant column:

'Experienced lad wanted. Able to ride work. Good refs. State age and weight.'

I applied. The following Saturday when I returned from work soon after six o'clock my mother handed me a letter from the racing stables. I was engaged on trial, fifteen shillings a week plus bed and board; report for work Monday week with a further direction to advise the time of my train's arrival when I would be met.

Not having informed my mother that I had applied for the job I handed over the letter. It was read. I stood there in expectation of another 'What next?' The letter was passed back in silence. I counted up to a slow five, then it came: 'Oh, well. I suppose you'd better get it out of your system.' Another pause; she looked at me. 'They say nothing about who pays the fare.'

'I expect they'll give it to me when I get there.'

'Very well. Find out how much it is and I'll draw it out of the piano money. And remember, see that you get it back before you start work. Is that understood?'

After breakfast, a week the following Monday morning, a piece of brown paper was put on the table and I watched a parcel being made of all my earthly possessions, spare shirt, two pairs of socks, a change of underwear and three handkerchiefs. 'And don't forget. See they're well aired before you put them on.'

As the train pulled out we said our goodbyes. I promised, like a dutiful son, to write regularly and listened to final instructions: 'Watch the company you keep and don't you ever forget your manners.'

What should have been the pleasure of the train journey and my first glimpse of England's green and pleasant land, was quite effaced by a severe attack of first-night nerves and the knowledge of the fact that, on arrival, I would be a stranger in a strange land. These bogies, having been allowed to take possession, summoned other niggling fears that fed on my shrinking self-confidence. I was engaged on probation only. The horses I would have to ride were thoroughbreds notable for savagery and high spirits. And there was no retreat. I had done too much boasting among my friends.

I was one of three passengers to alight when the train reached my destination and I was the last to emerge on the station's forecourt. A gaunt, unshaven man stood outside the station's door. He wore a cap and a corduroy waistcoat with black sleeves and flaps to its pockets. The top of a cut-throat razor peeped from one of the pockets. His corduroy trousers were baggy at the knees and his heavy boots had not been cleaned for some time. A well-fed, dock-tailed black mare was in the shafts of a dog-cart. Except for a porter trundling an empty truck, the man was the only person in sight. He appeared lost in thought and only came to earth when, standing a pace from him, I said, 'H'm.'

'You him for the stables?' he asked and, when assured, he clumped to the dog-cart saying, 'Come on,' and off we drove. He sat there in silence, reins in his large and dirty hands. He was leaning forward, elbows on knees, and he stared ahead morosely as though he were enduring a deep sorrow. I had hoped for conversation concerning the racehorses; whether, recently, there had been any deaths or horrid maimings by them among the stable lads. There was no point in my concealing the fact that I was afraid. Finally, after the mare had been trotting along smartly for about fifteen minutes I coughed and asked by way of preliminary: 'Do you work in the stables?'

'Farrier,' he said and again relapsed into silence.

'What are they like?—er—h'm—the horses?' By this my apprehensive being meant: 'Among them are there any given to the savaging of stable lads?'

He did not answer. I waited, then began to think that he might not have heard me. He was still staring dead ahead. Suddenly he turned his head away, spat, swung his head round and fixed me with a glittering stare, saying: 'An whoren woman is liken unto an open pit; men walketh round and falleth therein.' He then stared ahead and spat again, this time on the mare's rump, nor did he say another word until we turned off the road into the stable yard.

This was a long range of brick loose boxes, L-shaped, in whose centre was a circular lawn with a tall conifer in its middle. The farrier reached for the whip and made a savage swipe at a couple of cats. 'Bastards,' he snarled. 'Look at 'em. Everywhere.' I must confess that there was a rather large congregation. They were lying about in various attitudes of feline comfort. One, I noticed, perched on the edge of the half-door of one of the boxes was in silent communication with a chestnut racehorse whose head was poking out.

'Dirty, stinkin', muckin' yowlers—' the farrier said, bitterly. 'And those 're only what you see. Everywhere. Every-bloody-where they are. And you'll be havin' one.' His voice rose. 'I'll give you soddin' pets if I cop you. My Christ, I will.' He reined in. 'All right,' he concluded. 'Out with you.' He inclined his head to a long building at right angles to, and separate from, the stabling. 'In there. That's where they are.'

# 24

# 'New Boy – Just Joined'

The door was open. It gave on to a small porch, a flight of stairs and another door to the left of these. I stood on the mat within and listened at the closed door. No sound. I knocked and there was no answer. I turned the knob and peeped in. It was a long, bright room serving a double purpose. At the upper end stood a three-quarter-size billiards table, at its lower, near the fireplace, was a long, scrubbed dining-table with forms either side and a wooden armchair at its head and foot. There was a door either side the fireplace. The only sound was the slow, echoing tick of the pendulum clock whose hands stood at three thirty-five. I had not eaten since breakfast and had been feeling the pangs some time.

I left the door open and stood by the windows looking out and weighing up form. A six-foot-wide run of brick paving fronted the loose boxes; at the doors of each of these stood a brimming oak water-bucket all painted uniformly in bright colours. The yard itself was red gravelled and both this and the paving was swept clean.

At five minutes to four I heard the crunch of footsteps. A stoop-shouldered, shrivelled man in shirtsleeves, a cap, waistcoat, check riding breeches and box-cloth leggings came round the corner. From his gait I guessed him to be enduring trouble with his feet.

He stood on the mat, leaned his left hand on the stairs and, with his right clenched, began to beat a loud tattoo. 'Come on,' he bawled. 'Let's be havin' you, you lazy sods. Let's be seeing you, there. Toot sweet.'

He turned, saw me, came into the room and looked

MY MOTHER

around. 'Where's the other feller?' he asked, adding, when noticing my look of mystification, 'Wasn't there another lad on the train?'

'I didn't see anybody.'

'Ha! Not shown up. Then they wonder why we don't send their fares. Christ!' he went on and glared at me as though I were to blame. 'Times have changed since before the war. What's the world comin' to? Fifteen bob a week you're getting, eh?' He fixed me with a severe glance: 'When I was your age d'you know what I was getting? Half a bloody crown—when he remembered. Seven bastard years' apprenticeship, that was us. Arse kicked and a belt across the lug as soon as look.' He thrust his thumb ceilingwards: 'Beds? Ha! A kip on the straw and an old horse blanket for cover. Don't know you're born, you sods don't. An' now they're talkin' of trade unions. Goin' on strike, that's what we'll be hearin' next.' He turned and resumed thumping the stairs bawling afresh until he heard footfalls above. He turned back to me, looking me up and down: 'Those boots the only ones you've got?' I said that they were. 'Won't do,' he said. 'You'll have to buy a proper pair.' There was a clatter of youths down the stairs. 'Hey. You. Ginger,' he addressed a shrimp of a lad with carroty hair. 'Show him his bed.' I followed Ginger up the stairs.

It was a long dormitory, iron beds lining the walls either side, each separated by a tiny chest of drawers. Brass cup hooks were screwed into the walls next to some of the beds and, here and there, jackets, Sunday suits and overcoats were hanging therefrom. 'That's yours,' Ginger said. 'Over by the window. Stick your gear in the drawers.' He followed me and said, after a hesitant pause, 'Any money to lend?' He shrugged resignedly at my disappointing reply, explaining, 'I'm skint till pay day. Charlie Bint up at Malton—he sent me a hot tip from their stable.' He shrugged again. 'Down the field.'

'That man,' I said and indicated my boots. 'He said I've got to buy a proper pair.'

'Aye, an' he wants to buy himself a new pair o' feet. He's the head lad.' He lifted his left foot. 'He means you'll have to get a pair like these. Women's, they are. Narrow fitting. They're what's given him his bad feet.' He pointed to my boots. 'Never get those out o' racing stirrups if you were thrown. Poo, no. Hung up, that's what you'd be, dragged and kicked to death. You'll get a pair like these in the village. Eighteen bob. Oh, but you're skint too, aren't you? Never mind. I'll find you a pair of old 'uns to tide you over.'

His spontaneous generosity was affecting. He waved my thanks away and, when I apologized for my empty pockets, he grinned and waved again. 'I only wanted sixpence,' he said. 'You see, I've eaten my piece of marmalade tart. Usually save it for bedtime. I'm starvin' by then. If you'd've had a tanner to lend I'd've been off to the village tonight for a feed up of fish and chips. I *could* get 'em for nothin'. But ... Oh, I'll tell you about it some time.'

I remembered the train fare refund. It wasn't mine, of course. He brightened when I told him. 'The agent'll pay you now if you ask him,' he said. 'And I'll give you the tanner back on pay day. Shall I take you to his office? It's only round the corner.'

The agent, who had an artificial left arm and was referred to as 'the Major', gave me the money. After I had signed the receipt he said: 'Do you bet? Good. You would be well advised never to start. That goes for drinking, too.' I noticed that he was looking me over. He said, off-hand, as an afterthought, 'Some of the lads are short of the proper gear when they arrive. What about you?' I mentioned the footwear situation. He nodded. 'We have an arrangement with the shop in the village. Have you to send money home each week?'

'Five shillings, sir.'

'I see. I'll leave a letter for you in the saddle-room. Take it to the shop. We shall deduct half a crown a week from your pay. All right? Very well. I hope you'll find this a comfortable berth.'

Coming into the yard again the head lad, standing in the doorway of the tack room, bawled Ginger's name. 'Aw, get in a bag,' Ginger muttered, adding to me, under his breath, 'Leave him to me.'

Before the head lad had chance to inquire the reason for our tardiness Ginger said, 'The Major. Called him into the office.'

'He did, did he? Then you get on with it. And you', he said, addressing me, 'in here.' Another man was in the room. He was lean, middle-aged, coatless and wore jodhpurs whose strappings were ragged from wear. He had an air of pre-occupation and a habit of grinding his teeth which caused his cheek muscles to tighten in quick jerks. 'Give this feller Glen More, Sam, and—er—let's see. Aye, and Simonstown.' As he was speaking Sam, without comment, handed me a grooming kit in a zinc bucket. Still in querulous tones the head lad went on: 'Two o'clock they said she'd be here. Look at the time now. Afternoon stables and still no sign of the friggin' mare. That's the office for you. An' what about the stud groom they said they'd engaged? No sign of him, neither.' He was watching Sam who was reaching for a bridle with a heavy twisted bar bit, a stout surcingle, a check and a lunging rein. 'Yes,' the head lad said as 'Ooo-aaahing' he walked round the table leaning on his knuckles to take the weight off his feet, 'better have it handy just in case.'

I followed Sam across the yard to a loose box which stood on its own. Sam dropped the bridle, surcingle and reins outside on the brick paving, then opened the box doors. A big black racehorse stood blinking dozily as we entered. 'Simonstown' it said on the name board fixed to the far wall.

Sam lit a cigarette, stood in the doorway and said, 'All right,' as a signal to me to begin grooming operations. I might as well have been a harmless fly buzzing around for all the notice the horse took of me as I applied the soaked sponge to his eyes, nose and dock. I could feel Sam's critical eyes watching my every move. I had the horse's rug half off when Sam stopped me: 'Leave it on,' he said, then instructed me that, at this time of year, pampered racehorses never had their rugs removed completely even when being groomed. He was in the act of showing me how to fold the rug backwards and forwards when 'Ooo-oooing' and 'Aaah-aahing' the head lad looked in. The farrier, a folded sack under his arm, accompanied him. 'What did I tell you,' the head lad said in a paddy. 'Middle of afternoon stables and she's just arrived. Christamighty. Two o'clock, that's what they said in the office. Bring him out.'

To add to my bewilderment Sam countermanded his recent instruction. 'Off with his rug,' he said and walked to the door where he stooped and reached for the heavy bridle, reins and surcingle.

The moment Simonstown saw these all his drowsiness instantly disappeared. Up went his head and tail, fire came into his eyes, veins stood out along his neck and, trembling from poll to tail, began to voice a most alarming series of rumbling grunts, squeals and whinnies all of which, together with the way he began to dance about, persuaded me that he had suddenly gone raving mad.

Sam did not take the slightest notice of the animal's behaviour. He had him bridled, surcingled and check-reined in what appeared to be the blink of an eye. He snapped on the spring swivel of the lunging rein and handed the ten yards of its broad white webbing to me. 'Take him out,' he said which was, in a way, ridiculous, for I would like to have seen the man capable of keeping the demented creature in.

Outside it was not a question of where to take Simonstown:
he knew the way to go. Next the walled midden, twenty
paces distant and open to the sky, was a fenced-in compartment with a thick bed of tan. At its far end was a five-barred
gate, at its rear, leading into the yard, another gate on
runners with which to push it away at right angles. This had
a roller-bar top and, against it, a hunter mare was backed.

Ginger, on his way to the midden with a bulging muck
sack on his back, paused to watch, while the farrier's wife,
at the open window of her kitchen, began to clatter pots and
pans as though she disapproved of that which she seemed
determined to witness.

Simonstown by now had ceased to be a quadruped.
Sweating, screeching, grunting and squealing, he was on his
hind legs indecently and shamelessly exposing his masculinity, oblivious to all and everything other than the rump
of the object of his inordinate passion. She, for her part,
began to play the coquette making every effort, it seemed,
to meet her lover face to face, but her attendant would not
permit such civilities. Bawling and shouting he pushed her
back into place, nor were matters helped when, at the gate,
my charge, frothing freely at the mouth, began to bite her
buttocks. In the general confusion there were shouts and the
gate was rolled aside.

I realized that the shouts were being addressed to me. It
was the head lad's voice: 'Get a hold of his weapon, man.
Help him. *Help* him.' Simonstown, now a raving screaming
biped, flung himself on top of his love. Sam's arm was thrust
over my shoulder to help the consummation and Simonstown, now in possession, died the little death. His head
drooped, his eyes rolled, and, on a grunting sigh, he fell off
the mare, all interest in her gone. I was told to take him back
to his box and 'rug him up' while Sam, the head lad and the
mare's groom settled the business of the fees.

The farrier, sack under his arm and muttering to himself,

followed me. He was still mumbling in the box's doorway when, dizzy and confused, I took the harness from the lecherous horse and dumped it outside. The nightmare still had another episode. Pointing to a half-grown black cat with a white chest which was sitting in the sun licking itself a pace away, the farrier said: 'That's the one. Pick him up.' He repeated the order irritably when I looked at him in mystification. 'Go on,' he said. 'Pick him up.' I did so and he then took the sack from under his arm, put the cat's head and forelegs within and strung the bag's mouth round the cat's belly. 'Hold his tail and back legs,' he commanded. 'Go on. Get hold of 'em. Do as you're told.' Tail and legs were forced into my hands, he whipped out the cut-throat razor from his waistcoat pocket and, while muttering incoherently and throwing glances at his wife who was looking through the window, castrated the helpless, howling creature. After the surgery he put the struggling animal on the ground, cut the string and shook the cat out of the bag. It raced away to disappear among the higher branches of the conifer on the lawn.

I went back to Simonstown's box and closed my eyes.

# 25

# Holidays With Pay

' ... and like I've told you already, Old Crabbett's barmy,'
Ginger said, as, on the evening of my first day, we walked
the empty road in the gloaming to the village. He was
referring to the farrier whose monstrous behaviour still
plagued my mind. 'O' course, you know what's up with
him, don't you? It's his missis.'

'What about her?'

'She's younger than him. He's past it. Copped her bang
on the job. One o' the lads had her across a couple o' bales
of hay.' He laughed. ' "What's this? What's goin' on?"
That's what old Crabbett said. What a question.' He laughed
again, then his expression changed. 'Serve the bible-thumpin'
bugger right.' He went on, fiercely. 'But I've warned him.
"Touch my cat," I said, "and you'll get a prod in the guts
with my pitchfork." Aye, and he knows I would, too. As for
Ma Crabbett ... call that a tea she gave us tonight?' He
offered me a cigarette. 'Soddin' horses get better fed than us.'
He continued, on a note of warning. 'And you'll never see
that five bob, you know.' When he saw my questioning
look he repeated, 'Five bob. Five guineas, that's what
they've to pay for Simonstown coverin' a mare. Five guineas
fee and five bob the groom, but the dollar goes into the head
lad's pocket.' He shrugged. 'Oh, well, it's the same with us
and the bloody jockeys.' He cleared his throat and, using a
few bars from *Yankee Doodle*, sang: 'Stable lads do all the
work, but jockeys get the money.' He sighed 'Same all the
way down the line. Look at Sam. Stable jockey he is, really.
But when it comes to the big races who gets the mount?
Steve Donoghue, Carslake and Co. Suspended, Sam was.

Stewards had him on the carpet—bumping and boring, they said. If it'd been one of their horses you'd've heard no more about it, nothin' at all.' He interrupted himself to quiz me on my previous riding experience. 'Oh,' he went on, 'then you've not ridden short leathers before?' I said 'No.' The prospect of riding these skittish thoroughbreds even with customary long stirrup leathers would be test enough, but to be crouched, monkey-like, on their withers trying to hold and control animals capable of gymnastic performances such as I had seen demonstrated by Simonstown, caused me to be amazed at the folly of my being here. Additionally, there was the possibility of my being ignominiously thrown first time out, the head lad jerking his thumb in peremptory dismissal with: 'Office. Get your cards. Hoppit.'

'Here's a tip, then,' Ginger said. 'Hang on to the neck strap, the working lad's friend. Specially o' Monday mornings when the bastards've been standing in over the weekend. An' when we come to schooling the steeplechasers, sit well back at the open ditch.' In the event it turned out that there was no need for me to have handed myself over to be the sport of fear. An east wind was on the rampage the following Monday morning, its shrivelling blasts taking the fizz out of our pampered mounts, reducing them to a state of docility and thus giving me the chance to adjust to the necessary riding style.

We were entering the village. It was dark now, the sky full of stars.

'That's the fish-and-chip shop,' Ginger said. 'Oh, and I told you about it, didn't I? It's like this, you see.' He dropped his voice. 'Don't let on to the other lads. But—it's been going on for some time between Effie and me,' a nod towards the chip shop. 'Always on to me to go and lodge with 'em, Effie's ma is. She's a widow woman. I know the game o' course. Get me and Effie spliced. Goes out on purpose every Wednesday, *she* does and leaves Effie and me alone in the house. Mind you, it isn't a bad idea. It's a good business and Effie's a real worker. Not much to look at, I know. Still, you can't have everything; a livin's a livin' and a home's a home. Aye.' He murmured the last word thoughtfully, pulled his chin, gathered his brows, made a hissing noise and shook his head slowly. 'Oh, well,' he said, suddenly, forcing a smile, 'I'll leave it like it is and if my luck changes and I get her in the family way ... well, we'll see about it then. Here, let's be havin' that sixpence. I don't want either of 'em to know I'm skint.'

We were the only customers. The face of the fat lady behind the counter brightened when she saw Ginger. She half turned to the door leading to the living accommodation and, putting her cupped hand to the side of her mouth mariner-fashion, bawled over the noise of the fat sizzling in the fryer: 'Effeeee. Ginger's come.' Then, smirking at Ginger, added, 'She will be pleased. This *is* a surprise.' As though struck by an unwelcome thought her face dropped. 'You're not going to a race meeting—on Wednesday, I mean?'

'Naow,' Ginger said, 'flat racin' doesn't begin until the Lincoln.'

She smiled again. 'Only you know our Effie. Like a bear with a sore head Wednesdays and week-ends when you can't come round.' She winked, laughed, leaned over the counter and gave him a push. 'Get on with you, Ginge,' she said. '*I* don't know what it is you've got,' and she laughed again and turned to the fryer. I felt Ginger's elbow touch my arm.

A courting couple entered. Effie's mother served them out of turn. When they had gone she winked and said, 'I'll make fresh ones for you, Ginge. The usual, I suppose?'

'Aye,' Ginger said. 'Pennorth o' chips each, cup o' char and a plate o' bread and butter. Got to keep the weight down, y'know.' As he was speaking Effie's mother bustled to the living-room door. 'Bread and butter, pot o' tea for two and get away from in front of that mirror.' She returned to us, smiling indulgently, confiding: 'You know how it is when they're young. I was the same myself when I was her age. Here,' she held up two pieces of fish one in either hand, 'I was savin' 'em for Effie and me—best quality and fresh in today. But you and your friend can have 'em. I'd be ashamed if I was Ma Crabbett the way she half starves the lot of you up at the stables.' She flopped the fish in the fryer, turned and addressed herself to me. 'It's his own fault. The times and *times* I've told him. There's a good bed here for him and he'd be fed like a fighting cock.' This time Ginger nudged me with his knee.

'We know,' Ginger said, with a forced laugh. 'Then I'd have a belly like a mare in foal and be out of a job.'

More customers entered, then, from the living quarters and carrying a tray, came a plump, dumpy, dark-haired girl in her early twenties. She had a disconcerting squint, a lovely complexion and a faint moustache. She was flushed and smiling and, when we sat at the table by the window, she fussed and hovered, eyes and words for nobody but my companion until we had finished the food, Ginger, meanwhile, accepting all this devotion and attention in the manner of one who felt it to be no more than his due.

Effie came with us to the door. 'See you Wednesday, then?' she asked, eyes alight with eagerness.

'Shouldn't be surprised,' Ginger answered. 'So long. Well?' he said to me after we had walked away. 'What d'you think of her?'

I said that she had a very good complexion and he gave me an elbow dig and laughed. 'All over, too,' and he laughed again.

Out of a cloud bank low in the east sailed a huge and staring moon. Fields, trees and road were silvered with ghostly beauty. The air was still, the bare trees motionless like enchanted things.

'It was right, what I told her,' Ginger said, still with his problem. 'Start putting on weight and what then? You're out. Quick. Not that I'll ever get a mount in a race. Got to be apprenticed.' He threw me a warning glance. 'So if you've got any fancy notions in that line, mate—forget 'em.'

From the naked woods above the fields floated a long 'Whoooooooo.'

'Listen!' I exclaimed.

'It's only a blooming owl, man,' he said, with a touch of irritability, then went on with his chatter. I kept to myself the marvellous elation of having heard my first owl and I strained my ears for the repeat performance.

As we neared the stable yard a horrid, hoarse and ghastly shriek echoed through the night's silence. 'What's that?' I cried.

He looked at me, puzzled: 'Haven't you never heard a vixen before?'

I was glad that clouds once more obscured the moon. There was a general procession to the dormitory when we arrived. We went upstairs and, as we were preparing for bed, a late-comer came into the room. He was tipsy and talking to himself. 'Get in your bed,' the head lad said and turned out the lights. The other went on mumbling in the dark and I heard him flop heavily on to his bed. Presently, after tossing and turning awhile, he groaned, loudly. 'I want a woman,' he told the darkness.

'Somebody knit him one,' a voice replied.

'Who said that?'

'Bollocks.'

'Quiet, there, you lot,' from the travelling head lad.

Silence. The moon, large and bright, revealed herself. Somebody snored, but neither moonlight nor the snoring distracted for long. I felt a push and opened my eyes to the brightness of day. Ginger said: 'Hey, gerrup.'

In the months that followed I did not mention a word

either to him or any of the other lads of treasures that are as
fresh to me today as when I first glimpsed their intoxicating
loveliness all those years ago. The vernal splendour of ancient
oak and beech in the woods beyond the gallops; aisles shim-
mering with mote-filled sunlight and loud with the song of
birds whose names I did not know; trees whose trunks you
could stroke and rejoice to find that your palm was free of
soot.

High summer and solitary walks down perfumed by-lanes,
dusk gathering and moths upon the wing, then, on a night
without a moon and stars, lo! a whole hedgerow hung with
magic, the ghost-green light of clustered fireflies. Enchanted,
marvelling, I stood breathless in fairyland, delight marred by
the peeved thought that, but for rebellion, I would have
passed through this world, desk-fettered, with all this lost
unseen.

Spring and summer at daybreak before the flies were about;
chaff and banter among the lads out with the first string.
Dawn mists thick as wool and high as horses' bellies, not a
blade of grass to be seen; there we were in the clouds as
though away to pursue nubile Valkyries across the arches of
the sky. Leather creaking, heads tossing, the horses in training
on their toes being ridden at the walk along the tan track to
the prescribed marker post for the morning gallop. Then,
nearing the mark, prancings, snortings, grunts and buck-
ings; bits champing, ears pricked, eyes brightening as the
tip-toe mood of expectancy ran along the line. Off the tan
and on to the turf; a quick shortening of reins and, in
echelon and with a joyous and exhilarating leap, away at the
gallop, the rhythmic drumming of hooves bruising the grass
and adding a new and delightful fragrance to the glory of the
morning.

Welcome excursions to race meetings where your charge
was entered. One of the owners, a hearty, north-country
financial speculator who also backed musical shows, was at

most meetings and often drove down to the stables of a Sunday bringing with him parties of show girls and press photographers. Upon his patronage the stable largely depended, as did the bookmakers since he was a profitable customer. Apart from the excitement of the meetings there was the pleasure of striking up new acquaintances and renewing old friendships among the stable-lad fraternity: 'Look!' Ginger exclaimed. 'Jerry Marpole!' He pointed to one of the racecourse loose boxes where a thin and shabbily dressed lad stood chewing and staring at the ground as he leaned against the jamb of the door.

We joined him. 'Hello, there, Jerry. How's tricks, then? I see you came in fourth at Haydock Park.'

'Don't remind me,' Jerry said, wryly. 'Boxed in. Couldn't get out. Played bloody hell, he did.' His hand dipped into his jacket pocket and took out a pinch of crushed oats which he tossed into his mouth.

'Haven't you had any dinner?' Ginger asked and there was indignation in his tones.

'Not till he gives me my kip money.'

'Where're you lodging?'

Jerry inclined his head towards the straw in the box. 'Don't worry, Ginge. You know how it is. Plenty to eat,' he showed the oats on his palm, 'plenty to drink,' he kicked the water bucket, then jerked a thumb at the straw: 'a good bed to lie on and the boss thinks the world of me.' He grinned. We took him to the refreshment bar. 'And then,' Ginger said, after we had left him, 'we think we're badly done by. He's stuck like that till he's finished his apprenticeship. The poor bastard.'

For me my racing days were coming to an end. The post-war boom was beginning to crack. In early autumn news came to the yard that the north-country speculator was in financial difficulties and that his string of horses had to be sold.

Those of us who had to go said our goodbyes. Ginger came with me to the station. 'This is it, then,' he said as the train was signalled. 'You'd better know. Effie. She's in foal. My luck's changed at last, you see. Oh, well, that's my mind made up for me. At least I'll be sure of a kip and my grub. That shop's a good livin' an' like I said no man could get two better workers than her and her ma. So long, then, and good luck.'

# 26

# A Wide Lad

After the welcome-home ceremonies had been dispensed with I sensed conspiracy in the house. My sister who, in my absence, had finished her schooling and now was dressed in the part of the young woman, was obviously trying to conceal something. Mother turned to put the kettle on the fire as I placed my brown-paper parcel on the table; my sister, with a nervous cough, went into the parlour leaving its door open. I was about to sit when I was surprised to hear piano music. My mother, triumphant, turned from the fireplace and looked at me. I went to the parlour door. My sister was sitting at an old-fashioned instrument which had yellowing keys and a red silk-backed fretted front. She was playing a pleasingly simple melody with enviable confidence.

Proudly, Mother announced: 'Miss Bland got it for us at an auction. Paid for, every penny of it. Got it soon after you went away and kept it as a surprise. Isn't Betty doing well? God's been good to us, lad. Ay, deary me. He has indeed. There's poor Annie Boarder losing her little boy. Poor little thing. Oh, well! "He giveth and He taketh away." '

We heard Polly Mytton's voice. 'It's only me.' She entered, Alfie in attendance. 'Well, I never!' she exclaimed, looking me up and down. 'Doesn't he look well? What d'you think, Alfie?' Alfie and I grinned at each other. Although he had not put on any inches he had lost his half-starved look. 'Ay, deary me!' Polly went on: 'How time flies. Grown-up men they are now. Next thing we'll hear is they'll be getting wed.'

Mother, who was unfastening the string of my brown-paper parcel, said, with seeming irrelevance: 'There's a piano in

there, Polly. Good money it cost. He's a lot of practising to do
on that before there's talk of weddings.'

Another 'It's only me, love,' interrupted. It was Mrs
Boarder's deep voice. She came in as Mother, after having
examined my spare shirt, held it up. 'And who did your
washing?'

'We did our own.'

'Just look at this, Annie. What d'you make of it, Polly?'

Mrs Boarder's dark eyes swept from the shirt and looked
into mine. 'And that's never seen boiling water,' she said.

I explained the stable's lack of laundry facilities.

'And these darns,' Mother said, shaming me by exhibiting
my socks. 'Catch fishes with them, you could. And I don't
suppose you saved a penny from what was left of your wages.'

'Go on with you, lass,' Polly said, and laughed. 'He sent
five shillin' a week home regular.'

'Yes,' Mrs Boarder said, a trace of truculence in her voice,
'and that kept the buggerin' rent man quiet.' She shook her
head and sighed, heavily: 'And now they're only on three days
a week at some o' the mills—but workin' or not workin' that
rent goes on all the time.' Her eyes glowed. 'He's been told,
though, has that rent man for all of us in the street. Arrears or
no, grub for the kids comes first. And now there's our Hetty.
Manager did a bunk and left 'em all stranded up in Scotland
with not a penny piece among 'em. She'd be better off behind
Woolworth's counter at a quid a week. But, oho, no. She won't
be told. Listen to me, letting the dumps get me down.' She
looked at me. 'What're you going to do now you're home, lad?'

'For goodness' sake give him time to sit down,' Polly protested. 'He's only just come in.' She changed the subject to one
of feminine generalities, at which Alfie and I withdrew to the
street. For a while there was an awkwardness between us.
Despite having been to the wars he still wore the air of self-
effacing meekness. Our halting conversation was interrupted
by Mickmac who came round the corner and stopped on

seeing me. He grinned. 'By gum!' he said. 'You're proper sunburned.' His jacket was ragged, his cheeks sunken, face and hands dirty. The thumb and forefinger of his right hand were wrapped with bits of rust- or blood-stained rag. When he learned that I was looking for work he astonished me by saying, 'Nobby'll give you a start,' then, seeing my puzzlement, continued, in admiring tones, 'He's opened a box works. He lets you work as much overtime as you've a mind. Even Sat'day afternoon. I've just put four hours in. It's piece work. He's making money hand over fist, isn' he, Alfie?'

Alfie tapped his temple. 'He's got it up here. Just the same in the army. Crown and anchor, the lot, he was running. Won a packet.'

The Nobby whom I saw that evening was transformed. He was smartly dressed and, though the evening was warm, he wore a light overcoat, tailored, with a velvet collar; his head-gear was a black bowler set at an angle; his expression a mixture of condescension, pained boredom and aloofness. He lit a cigarette but did not offer me one and he looked at me sidewise as one suffering from a stiff neck. 'Yes,' he said, 'they told me you'd gone doo-lally about the gee-gees.' Then he made a wry face, continuing: 'You'll never make any money out o' them unless you're the bookie. What did Charlie Dacre say years ago? Horses? Finished. Motors, that's the lark. Bought two. Ex-army. Own transport. Can't go wrong an' I got 'em for next to nothing. Mind you—' He winked, dipped his hand into his pocket, withdrew it and made a furtive, backhand movement as though passing a bribe. 'Get it? Quartermaster at the depot. New engines, new tyres, full set o' spare parts. We-ell. I mean to say ... Dead easy. Got to know the ropes, that's all.' He rubbed his chin, thoughtfully. 'A job, eh? Let's see. What can we do for you? Tell you what. You've worked in an office. I'll give you a start in the shop. Three-pence a box, that's the rate: as much overtime as you want to put in. And you can type the letters and be my sekertary when

6

I want you. We can work that out paid by the hour. I'd have a girl but—oh, well, you know them. Skirts they're wearin' up to their knees these days an' it doesn't do to mix business wi' pleasure. Anyway, that's the job. An' with all this short time that's startin' ... Well, there it is. Want it? Right. Eight o'clock Monday mornin'. I'll be there.'

Nobby's place of business in the gasworks' district was a semi-derelict building whose lower floor had been a twelve-stall stable. The partitions had been removed and the entrance enlarged to admit the garaging of his ex-army lorries. A quarter of the area had been boarded off and part glazed. 'Office' it said on one of the doors: 'Mr T. Clarke'. 'Private' it said on the other.

Mr T. Clarke, with an air of busy preoccupation, took me to the office, pointed to the typewriter and said: 'That's it. Ex-army, you know,' winked and again performed the furtive, backhand routine. He showed me a sheet of his business stationery which was headed 'BOXO CO.' with his name below as Managing Director. 'Pays to advertise,' he said. 'Oxo, y' see—Boxo. Get it?' The business he ran was simplicity itself, he explained. He had a contract with a firm of tea importers in the vast Trafford Park industrial area a mile distant. This obliged him to keep the importer's premises clear of the end-less supply of empty tea chests and boxes. These, renovated, were sold to a big firm of toffee manufacturers and others as packing cases for their products.

'Right,' he said, taking the letter heading from me, 'I'm busy. Do the letters when I get back. Come on. You'd better get crackin' earnin' some money on the boxes.' I followed him up a flight of stairs to what, at one time, had been the hayloft. This echoed with the hollow banging of hammers. There was an open off-and-on loading gap, six feet wide or so, in the wall looking on to the street and it reached from floor to ceiling. A roughly made door, hinged to the inside brickwork, was pushed flat against the wall and on this was painted:

BOXO CO
Packing Case Mftrs
& General Carriers.

With the exception of an elderly man with a bronchitic
wheeze and a stoop, the staff consisted of youths and young
men. Everybody called the old man 'Dad' and his home was
round the corner. A card in the ground-floor window of this
said 'Good Clean Beds for Single Men'. Its dining-room was in
the cellar and passers-by, glancing down, could see the lodgers,
nearly all of them old men, waiting at the fireplace to take
turns frying their evening meal.

Messrs Boxo's work benches were improvised, being packing cases turned upside down. All the window frames were
devoid of glazing. Nobby glanced round, then said, sternly
and rudely, to the old man, 'Hey. Where's Dooley, then?'

'Dad', holding his hammer and coughing nervously,
shuffled across to Nobby and said, 'Had to take his wife to
hospital. Said he'd be back afore twelve.'

Nobby looked affronted. 'Hospital?' he said, indignantly.
'*I'm* not payin' him wages to take his wife to hospital. This
means *I'll* have to fetch the flamin' load or you lot'll be
standing about earnin' nowt—aye, and blamin' me for it.
And where's Baxley?'

'Doctor. Under the doctor. Sent word round,' Dad explained and passed the back of his hand under his nose to
remove a dew-drop. 'Fingers all festered agen,' he said.

'Oh, they are, are they? Then put him here on in his place.'
He jerked his head towards me, then went off downstairs
muttering, 'One bloody thing after another with you lot.'

We heard the lorry engine spluttering below. The elderly
man, after pointing the haft of his hammer to an upturned
box, said to me: 'Work there,' then, muttering obscenities
concerning our employer, shuffled to his station and resumed
hammering.

Mickmac came over to me. 'You take 'em from there,' he said, indicating a stack of boxes. 'Here y'are. I'll show you,' adding, under his breath, 'Watch 'em. They're all on the dodge to get the good 'uns.' He reached for the next available box. One of the boards in its side was bashed in. 'Nail a patch over that. Find your own nails. There y'are, them stickin' out of the edges or any you can scrounge off the floor. Got to straighten 'em, o' course. An' see the hoop iron? Got to break it off—like this.' He took the hoop iron between thumb and forefinger and worked it up and down quickly until it snapped. 'You want rags round your fingers. Get blood poison if you don't, like Harry Baxley. Then you make a lid.' He showed me how to cannibalize the necessary from boxes beyond repair. 'Trouble is,' he concluded, 'he's supposed to keep us goin' with boxes. But you know Nobby. If he hears of a carryin' job goin' or anything else that'll bring him in money—' he shrugged, 'he leaves all of us here hangin' about waitin'.' He grinned: 'Ne'er heed, though. You can always put in the overtime to make your coppers up.'

For a moment he stood there watching my clumsy efforts, then, with an impulsive gesture, he took his hand from his pocket and held it out to me. His palm was heaped with nails that he had straightened. I looked at him. 'Go on,' he said, with unaffected generosity, 'take 'em. They'll start you off.'

Like Mickmac, the rest of the staff seemed to accept the working conditions with patient resignation. More to be remarked was their infectious cheerfulness for, as we hammered away, an irrepressible character known as 'Jockey', a lad with merry eyes and a sunny disposition, burst spontaneously into the latest popular song:

> 'When you wore a tulip, a sweet yellow tulip
> And I wore a big, red rose ...'

We all joined in.

# 27

# Men of Business

Nobby's unswerving devotion to self-advancement was fascinating. Consideration for us, as Mickmac had said, never seemed to concern him in the least. All too often when we had cleared the supply of boxes we were left standing in unpaid idleness waiting the return of the lorries which had been hired out to firms in urgent need of occasional transport. His indignant attitude to anybody's complaints was blunt and definite. 'You can catch up by workin' overtime, can't you? An' understand this: my business is bein' run for me. If it doesn't suit ... okay. Ask for your cards. I don't know what the hell some o' you think you are. You're all quick enough off the bloody mark when you hear of a job that suits you better. Blimey, not half. And I'm left in the lurch.'

It was his custom, after one of these clashes, to stamp off, still simmering, to his office whither he summoned me to attend his correspondence. 'Can you beat it?' he demanded of me. 'Here's me, finding the sods work and this is the thanks I get. Well, they can all go to hell and back, the lot of 'em.'

Presently he confided that he had other fish to fry. 'I'm branchin' out,' he said. 'Now that this is a goin' concern I'm gettin' rid. That's the secret o' business, knowin' when to pull out.' He lit a cigarette. 'There's old Wheelam. Look at him. Hung on and hung on. Two years ago he could have flogged the lot of his mill shares at five pounds ten a time. But, no, the greedy old bastard thought they were going up to six.' He made a wry face and tapped his forehead. 'If he'd 've used this he'd have picked up a clear profit of fifty thousand quid and more. Cash. Retired, Bournemouth.

Look at his shares now, and him supposed to be the know-all business man. Drug in the market aye, and on some of 'em he owes fifteen shillings a piece on call. Tell you this, and you can have any money on you've a mind, he'll be dead in a year. Cotton? Finished. Look at this.' He showed me an auctioneer's catalogue of a cotton mill in the hands of the Receiver. 'You know what happened at the auction? Not a single bid. Sellin' the machinery piecemeal—and that's where I'm steppin' in. Knock-down prices, nearly as cheap as pig iron, that's what looms and spinnin' frames're fetching now.' He put his head back and looked at me, craftily, down his nose. 'Knowin' where the body's buried, that's the game, lad.' He gave me the thumbs-up sign. 'It's all fixed. Oh, aye, it's all arranged. There's half a dozen out o' work engineers I've interviewed—old fellers, y'know, can't get a job. They can do all the overhaulin'—and all those looms and spinnin' frames, d'you know who I'm floggin' 'em to? India and the Chinks. Aye, well, let's get on wi' these letters. Oh,' he interrupted himself, 'and if a woman named Agnes rings say I've gone to London. An' if you start chasin' after skirt, take my tip—go where you're not known.'

His spiteful dismissal of Mr Wheelam's financial disaster was an attitude not shared by everybody.

'Go on with you, Annie Boarder,' Polly Mytton said when the matter was under discussion in our kitchen, 'it doesn't become any of us to start crowing when somebody's down on their luck.'

'Crowing?' Mrs Boarder protested, indignantly. 'And as for being down on your luck, my God, Polly, we've been down on that all our flamin' lives and from the looks of it that's the way it'll be to the bitter end.'

Mother sighed. 'He's an old man now and alone. We mustn't forget that, Annie,' she said. 'Yes, it's not as though he's young.'

'I wouldn't mind it if he'd stop his everlasting whingeing

and whining,' Mrs Boarder retorted. 'Old man, did you say? More like a child, he is. It's the same every day when I go in to clean up and give him his grub.' She fell into an imitation of him: ' "They keep sending for more money all the time, Mrs Boarder. But I haven't got it. They've taken it all." And he won't listen. I keep telling him, if he's got nowt they'll get nowt like the rent man when we're skint. But I might as well save my breath. And as for crowing—I like that. You can't call working for him for nowt crowing, Polly, and that's what I'm doing these days.'

'We know you are, love,' Polly said, soothingly, 'and I didn't mean you at all.' She shook her head. 'The man's losing weight fast and that's a bad sign. Clothes're flappin' about him like flags. Took him a bowl o' broth I'd made but there he was, just sittin' there starin'. Ay, deary me.' Her heavy sigh produced one similar from my mother who murmured, sympathetically: 'We never know what's in store for us, lass. Who'd have thought it? All those thousands he said he had. All gone.'

This was too much for Mrs Boarder. She slapped the table and got to her feet, her dark eyes afire. 'You two ought to take the hat round and go collecting for him,' she declared. 'Here we are, mills on three days a week, wages being cut in the mines and the colliers forced to work a longer day—then you two ready to shed tears because old Wheelam's lost a fortune.' She began to knock the table with a rigid forefinger. 'I'll tell you this, if any one of us'd had sixty thousand pennies, never heed pounds, we'd have known what to do.'

Soon Nobby demonstrated that, as an employer, he, too, knew what to do. Wearing a new suit and the tense air of cunning watchfulness which always appeared when one of his deals was at a critical stage, he called me into his office one morning. An empty lorry belonging to the firm stood under the loading door; the other was due back from Trafford Park with another supply of boxes although there was no room for them above stairs. Yesterday, on Nobby's instructions, the drivers had been told to 'stack the place up'.

When in his office I noticed that he had 'stacked up' in another particular: whisky, gin, a syphon, glasses and a box of cigars were on his desk. A cigar smouldered between his fingers and filled the place with its aroma.

'Told you I was sellin' out, didn' I?' he said, with a conspiratorial wink. 'I've got a feller interested.' He waved his hand towards the liquor, then raised an imaginary glass: 'One o' those. Anyway, he's due any minute.' Sounds of footsteps interrupted. He rose and glanced through the glazing. 'Oh,' he said, resuming his seat, 'these're the fellers I asked the Labour Exchange to send round,' another wink. 'Makes it look well. Tell 'em to wait.' When I returned he said, briskly, 'Yes. Now. Listen. Get some paper in that typewriter. When the feller comes nip upstairs and tell 'em to start loading the lorry. And keep that typewriter rattlin' all the time.'

The 'feller' was a plump man whose hair was thinning and streaked with grey. His ruddy complexion conflicted with that of his nose which had a tinge of blue. He licked his lips perpetually and, from his jovial expression and frequent chuckles, one would have thought that, to him, life was a huge joke.

'I won't say no, lad,' he said, grinning when Nobby offered him a drink and a cigar. He drained the measure at a couple of gulps then said, 'Best o' luck,' and passed back the glass which Nobby replenished.

'Luck, eh?' Nobby said, after he had been wished this again. 'Having plenty o' that these days, thank God. Can't go wrong.'

'Me neither,' the other said. 'Mustn't grumble. Mustn't grumble at all. Gorrouta cotton in plenty o' time. Aye, I did that. Made a packet. All I'm lookin' for now is summat to keep me occupied, and bugger Bognor. Bloody hole. Let her stay there if she wants to. But I told her: I'm gerrin' back north. Soddin' bridge and whist and Lah-di-bloody-dah. "Laughing at you," I told her, "laughing at you all the time." But they don't laugh at this feller. Not bloody likely, lad.'

Nobby went to work. An hour later, after the man had been shown around, the deal was done on a handshake. Nobby then offered the benefit of expert advice. 'There's the profit,' he said, slapping the open ledger. 'And if you want to raise it: simple. Cut the rate, that's all. Planned to do that, anyway. Cut it to tuppence a box. There's thirty-three and a third savin' on the wage bill at one go. Not all at once, mind. Ha'penny this month and a ha'penny next. An' as for whether they'll take it—' he waved his hand then pointed to the men outside. 'There's your answer. All of 'em waiting for a job. Anyway, it stands to sense, doesn't it? Well, I mean ... Read the papers. What does the Gover'ment say? There's got to be wage cuts all round. Look at the miners. Twenty-five per cent off wages, aye, *and* a longer working week.' He made a face. 'As for half of 'em upstairs, you know why they're workin' here, don't you? Unemployment pay run out. Once they get another thirteen stamps on their cards, then what? Pttth! Off—and signing on the dole agen.'

When I reappeared at my bench I was surrounded by my workmates. Jockey danced a few jubilant steps when I reported what had happened. 'Goodo!' he exclaimed. 'That feller looks a real sport. Tell you what: what about us all asking him for a rise in the rate?' There was a general falling of faces when I warned them of the drastic proposal Nobby had made.

Numbed by the news 'Dad' sat heavily on his bench and stared at the littered floor. 'Tuppence a box,' he murmured. 'Oh, hell, how am I goin' to manage?'

He still sat there staring when we resumed work, nor when, irrepressibly, Jockey struck up with 'Pack up your troubles', did he appear to hear our singing.

The new regime was short-lived. It disintegrated when our jovial employer began to see grotesque creatures emerging from the walls. For us who were young, unskilled work was to be had on cut-price terms. With 'Dad' it was different. What happened to him I do not know.

# 28

# *A Man With A Mission*

He soon made himself and his beliefs known to the neighbourhood. It was his views, too freely expressed at his work, that had earned him the sack. Undeterred, he had found employment at a small engineering works locally and, with his wife, two children and father-in-law, had come to live near by. James Moleyns his name, an intelligent-looking man in his mid-thirties.

Where Mrs Boarder was concerned he started off on the right foot. Returning to her a borrowed kitchen chair from which he had made a Sunday morning speech to the street, he saw, on her wall, the framed enlargement of an army intake. He looked at it, turned to her and said, 'Anybody of yours here, Missis?'

'Two of 'em,' she answered and indicated husband and son.

'Jack and Harry Boarder,' he murmured, then pointed to himself in the picture.

'It's a miracle you're here to tell the tale, lad. More than I can say for my husband and our Harry.' She pointed to the two framed official certificates on the wall which testified that Corporal John Boarder and Trooper H. Boarder slept for ever in foreign fields. 'Two bits o' paper, that's all there is to show. And what did the General get that sent them there?'

Moleyns shook his head and said, wryly: 'A hundred thousands pounds — "from a grateful country".'

We, grouped in silence at the door, listened to their bitter exchanges on the war and its aftermath. Mrs Boarder concluded: 'I didn't understand half o' what you were

spoutin' about in the street, but any time you want the chair
the door's always open. If I'm not in just help yourself.'

That he had other interests was revealed during November's municipal elections when he, storm-lamp in hand,
called at our house one foggy night canvassing Labour's
interests. Mother invited him in and, to prove that he was in
the presence of the converted, opened our bookcase and
showed him her father's treasures.

'Yes,' she said, pride and defiance in her voice, 'thirty
years and more ago when I was a young woman he'd have
us all out at I.L.P. meetings selling Blatchford's *Merrie
England*. But it was like talking to that wall where some
working people were concerned. Yes, fifteen to eighteen
shillings a week, that's all some of them were bringing home
—if they got in a full week's work. "Here he is," some of the
idiots said. "One of those Socialists that wants us to share all
we've got." ' She shook her head. 'It was enough to turn your
hair grey—and him earning three times what they were
getting. It used to madden me, it did, really, but I never
saw him lose his patience once.'

James Moleyns smiled. 'Once you lose that—' a shrug.
'Persuasion, that's the ticket. Though,' he confessed, 'I
must say that the Tory working man drives me to the limit
sometimes. But when I start to get on edge I know it's time
to call it a day. Oh!' he exclaimed, when he saw the collection of operatic and Hallé concert programmes. We found
we were entertaining a rabid enthusiast of Wagner. Politics
were relegated awhile as, eyes bright and burning, he raved
on his idol. 'Have you read Bernard Shaw's *The Perfect
Wagnerite*? No? I'll lend you my copy.' He looked at me.
'Look,' he said, 'if you'd like to hold the lamp till I've
finished your street we'll go home and you can have the
book now.'

His wife who had eyes made to go with smiles was taking
a batch of loaves from the oven when we went into their

kitchen. The steel fender and fire irons gleamed silver on the white hearthstone. Over the mantel was a framed photograph of him and his bride standing in the church porch. It was flanked either side by pictures of Robert Burns, Bernard Shaw, Wagner, Lenin and Keir Hardie. A short-sighted old man who, I learned later, was Ben Brierley, his father-in-law, sat in a rocking chair under the window holding a newspaper almost to his spectacled nose. Behind the old man, from the chimney breast to the window wall, were crowded bookshelves, the top one carrying a row of box files, parcels of political pamphlets and a small stack of gramophone records. His collection of Bernard Shaw's works was the paperback edition. He wrote my name and the date on a slip of paper, clipped this to the next volume then, grinning apologetically, passed *The Perfect Wagnerite* to me saying: 'I like to keep track.'

Ben Brierley, disturbed from his paper, looked up. 'You're back, then. Must be mad going out in a fog like this.' He looked at his daughter who was brewing tea. 'And him supposed to be intelligent. Talk some sense into him, that's what you ought to do, Helen.'

'There's enough argument between you two without making more,' she answered.

'Argument?' her father retorted. 'It's plain common sense, that's what.' He glanced sternly at James Moleyns. 'Foreman, that's what you'd have been if you'd learned to keep that big trap of yours shut.'

'Well, he didn't keep it shut, Dad,' his daughter said, 'and he's not the foreman.'

'But he could ha' been.' Ben looked at me. 'Marked him, that's what they did. Gave him the bullet.' Once more he glanced sternly at his son-in-law. 'I should ha' thought that would have taught you a lesson. You've a couple o' childer upstairs and don't you forget it, Jim Moleyns.'

James smiled. 'Your handsome daughter's not likely to let me forget that.'

The old man grunted. 'Contentment, that's what you young 'uns ought to learn and less o' this always stirring up trouble ... '

'Look, Dad,' James said, patiently, 'if any trouble's being caused it can't be blamed on us. The war's been over for years and where's the homes fit for heroes? No signs of these houses coming down. They say we won the war—and where are the winnings? In the pockets of the big boys and it's mugs like us being asked to take the can back as per usual. Rationing over, did you say? It's back agen. Ten per cent off wages and a longer working day, that's what the coal owners are shouting for.'

'Hush, Jim, hush,' his wife murmured. 'Not so loud. You'll waken the children.' She poured tea and passed it to us.

He dropped his voice but not his fervour. 'We all know what's in the wind. They've got it all worked out, the Employers' Federation. Defeat the miners first then put it across the rest of us. But one of these fine days they'll go too far.'

'All right, Jim. All right,' Mrs Moleyns said, 'that'll be enough for one night.' She looked at me. 'He'll finish up in Parliament though.' She smiled. 'If somebody gave him the extra little push I wouldn't be at all surprised if he ended up taking Holy Orders. Oh, go on with you, Jim,' she said when she saw him about to speak. ' "Christian Socialism"— I did read that article you wrote, you know.'

He shook his head and he, too, smiled. 'Are you in a union?' he asked me.

'The Shop Assistants,' I informed him and told him of the new job I had landed in a Manchester home trade warehouse.

'That's the ticket. Unity's the answer, aye, and education. Look ... ' He became eagerly persuasive.

'Drink your tea, Jim,' his wife interrupted.

'All right, lass. All right,' he said, irritably, then addressed himself to me again. 'We're starting classes at the Labour Club. We've our own tutors. We don't favour the Workers' Education Association—biased the wrong way. National Council of Labour Colleges. Marxist slant, that's us. Nothing to stop anybody from getting a scholarship to Oxford—Ruskin College.'

Their clock struck eleven.

'Never mind going to Oxford, Jim,' Mrs Moleyns said. 'Drink up and let's be getting to bed.'

# 29

# Battersby's Gentlemen

Messrs Battersby & Co Ltd, of which I now was an employee, was of old-established and high reputation. It was a huge departmental store whose business, with those of others like it in Manchester's centre, was to supply retailers throughout the land with drapery, clothing, bedding, furniture and all suchlike on wholesale terms.

Employees of other Home Trade houses jeeringly referred to us as 'Battersby's Gentlemen'. This might have derived from the fact that the managing director of the company was a member of the Cheshire Hunt. He advertised this by appearing sometimes at the general offices accoutred in hunting pink, white breeches, boots and top hat. His transit to his office from his chauffeur-driven car parked outside the main entrance was conspicuous and leisurely. Instead of calling heads of departments to his office, the Mountain, in his colourful array, visited the respectful Mahomets to discuss and query items in the sheafs of invoices held in both hands. A few minutes before ten o'clock he turned his back on commerce, passed through the main doors, acknowledged the commissionaire's smart salute and was driven away from Manchester's wintry gloom to horse, hounds and the huntsman's horn where I, too, unbeknown to him, would like to have been.

The nagging, permanently dissatisfied and demanding gentleman that lived within me was soothed, to some extent, by the nature and business of the department to which I was assigned. In the catalogue this appeared under the title 'Carpets and Furniture', and it included a piano section.

The latter was largely a convenience for the retailers.

These, hearing that a friend or customer was contemplating the purchase of a piano, dropped the hint, 'I can get it for you wholesale.' If the friend or customer responded the retailer telephoned or wrote, advising us of his coming with the customer, instructing us to add thirty-three and a third to our wholesale price from which, in our presence and the customer's, he generously deducted a ten per cent discount and everybody was made happy.

My fugitive happiness was in the daydreams engendered by tribute from the Middle and Far East whose costly bales arrived infrequently to satisfy demands of the opulent and the discriminating. Splendid carpets appropriate to Chinese emperors, sultans' palaces and the marbled floors of jewelled rajahs, gorgeously patterned things on which houris might have danced. All from Smyrna, Bokhara and other magic places which neither I nor any of the other salesmen was ever likely to see.

'That's what you call *real* quality,' Tom Besant said to me. He was my senior by a few years; we had interests in common both in music and politics. He turned the corner of the carpet, looked at its back and then at me: 'Like to estimate how many tufts to the square inch?' I confessed inability. He pointed to a machine-made Axminster square. 'Look at the back of that for a guide. Go on. You're learning something.' The comparison was absurd. Tom smiled. 'Thirty to the square inch, that one. This—' he stroked the import lovingly —'four hundred, mate, and every one hand-knotted. Work of art, and God alone knows what the poor devils who made it were paid.' He was unmarried because, he said, his thirty shillings a week wages would put too much of a strain on things. 'In any case,' he had explained, 'I'm not in any hurry. I'm in the running for old Bartholomew's job. Retires in a couple of years. Midlands and the whole of Wales.' He nudged me, winked and grinned. 'Just the job, boy. You can always make a bit on the expense account.

Then there's the life.' He fetched a yearning sigh. 'Commercial traveller! On the move all the time. New towns, new places.'

At lunch-time many of Messrs Battersby's Gentlemen patronized a cellar eating-house which, for ninepence, served hash, bread, a sweet and a cup of strong tea. The place was known affectionately as 'Dirty Minnie's'. If any of the Gentlemen absented themselves from their usual places at the scrubbed-top tables it was assumed that, for them, today's diet would be 'flag hash', that is, the lunch-break spent strolling the flagstones of Manchester's main streets. It was adopted by those saving for marriage or for holidays. Among those who regularly practised this austerity was Duckworth, a lanky, morose young man, thin as a rail, who wore steel spectacles on his beak-like nose and who was responsible in our department for the stock of linoleum.

'I'd watch it,' Tom Besant said as we sauntered the busy streets after we had had our ninepennyworth. 'He'll kill himself, you'll see. Flag hash twice a week and walking to work and back every day, hail, rain or shine. All to save up to get wed. He's shown you her photo, o' course?'

He had. The object of Duckworth's doting affection had been photographed 'draped', as the current fashion was called. Head, shoulders and as much bosom as decency and daring permitted were shown tantalizingly naked, floating in a mist of veils cunningly arranged to tease and hypnotize masculinity.

'As for her maidenhead,' Besant went on, 'that stays in one piece till they're wed. Poor old Ducky. Oh!' He interrupted himself and snapped finger and thumb. 'Just remembered. Got to see Cliff Marsh. Party Executive meeting.' We changed direction. 'Of course,' he said, resuming, 'you can't really wonder at it, can you?'

'What?'

'Why, the thieving that's going on. You know how much

they trust us.' On leaving the warehouse every night each employee had to pass a couple of sentinels. All attaché or other cases had to be opened for inspection and every parcel needed a 'pass out' ticket signed by the departmental head. 'It's the same in every warehouse. But they ask for it, the wages we're paid. Skint, every one of us, by Thursday. Aye, and the overtime lark, look at that. It's never "Will you work tonight?" It's "You're on overtime". No previous notice. Look at last Thursday. I'd booked for the Hallé. Made no diff. Sixpence, tea money, that's all. Two hours, threepence an hour and had to scoot like a scalded cat to catch the second half of the concert.'

We stopped outside a wholesale provision company's place of business near the Cathedral. A horse-drawn lorry was pulled up outside and this was loaded with sides of bacon wrapped in sacking, four sides to the bale. Each was stencilled 'Latvia'. Cliff Marsh, who wore pince-nez and had the look of an ascetic, was checking the bales as they were unloaded.

'Right, Tom,' he said, after having been given the message. 'I'll be there.' He turned to one of the men unloading. 'Get this out of the way,' he said, pointing to a bale lying on the pavement. Its wrapping was torn and, through the rent we saw movement, a writhing mass of maggots.

'Good food wasted,' Tom murmured.

'Wasted?' Cliff said. 'What d'you mean, "wasted"?'

'Well, I ask you. Look at it. It's crawling.'

'Accidents happen, boy,' Cliff answered and grinned. 'Scientific treatment, that's all it wants. A wash-down with borax, a nice long dry off in the smoke stoves and what have you got? Prime smoked bacon, comrade. Waste not want not.' He closed his left eye. 'Like your grandma said, the tricks of the trade. What the eye doesn't see ... '

The Town Hall clock struck one.

'That's us,' Tom said. 'Back to the old grind.'

# 30

# *Turning the Screw*

'I know nothing about gold standards and there's nothing I want to know,' Duckworth said, flatly. It was lunch-time and Duckworth, pint pot on the counter in front of him, was spooning, from a screw of newspaper, a coalescence of sugar, condensed milk and tea leaves which he then dropped into the pot. A tissue-wrapped package was next the pot and this, we knew, was his midday meal, a couple of rounds of cold toast and margarine. 'Another thing,' he went on, staring at Tom Besant, 'what d'*you* know about it? Them in the gover'ment, they know what's best for the country. They're experts.'

'Experts in cutting wages,' Besant retorted: 'Honest Stan Baldwin and Mr Bank-of-England Montague—a bright pair o' wizards.'

'Oh aye? Well, I'd rather put my money on them than your trade union leaders. Trouble, that's what they're stirrin' up. Look at him over the miners—A. J. Cook,' he made a face. 'Him and his "Not a penny off the pay, not a minute on the day." He gives me the bellyache, he does.' He picked up the *Daily Herald* borrowed from Besant and then moved towards the W.C.—washroom which served as dining-hall for those who were practising economies. He paused at the door to announce, querulously: 'And I'll tell you summat else. They'll have another think coming.'

'What's the bleat now?'

He held up the newspaper. 'This here General Strike they're starting tonight. It's like my girl said: let them as want to join in go and get on with it. Not me. I've gorra good job here an' I'm riskin' it for nowt nor nobody.' He disappeared. We heard the tin kettle being filled, then the gas ring pop as he put a match to it.

Besant raised his brows and put his head on one side. 'Blackleg number one,' he said. 'Ah, well, what can we expect from Messrs Battersby's underpaid Gentlemen? Five per cent union membership. Yes, Brother Greenwood, and *I'll* tell *you* something: if you come out in support you'll find yourself in the dole queue before I can say "Workers of the World — unite!" '

That warm May night as the clocks struck twelve the rhythm of labour throughout the land stopped abruptly. Railways, docks and public transport; engineering shops, cotton mills and all trades affiliated to the Trades Union Congress downed tools in support of the miners in Britain's first and only General Strike.

Enthusiastic young men of the middle classes, volunteers to the organization for the Maintenance of Supplies, came forward to man footplates, drive trams and buses and discover a variety of new aches and pains by experiencing rough manual labour at the docks and elsewhere.

'Bastards,' Jack Lashwood said, bitterly, to the congregation of strikers on our street corner. He was an elderly collier, a tall, scrawny man with a thin neck and blue marks on his skull which showed through his close-cropped hair; relics, they were, of roof falls. 'I know what I'd like to do with 'em.'

'It's a game for 'em, Jack,' James Moleyns said.

'Game?' he retorted, with pop-eyed indignation. 'Six loaves of bread a week, that's what a two shillin's wage cut means to me. Game? Kids goin' short o' grub? It's a fine bloody game.'

'They don't know, Jack,' James persisted. 'Two shillings is summat they leave under the plate for the waiter. I tell you, if they saw the inside of a working man's kitchen and the kids going short they'd be the first to start writing letters of protest to the papers.'

'Listen to the "ifs". They want to see us licked and crawling back on the bosses' terms.' He spat and, glaring all round, held out two enormous hands. 'I'd like to get these on some of 'em, be-Christ I would.'

'The buggers,' Mrs Boarder exclaimed, arms akimbo. 'If it was left to me to do the coal-getting down those hell-holes there'd be a lot of rich fat-gutted buggers shiverin' in front of empty grates. Less pay an' longer hours is it? May God forgive them mine owners. Aye, and them in Parli'ment too.'

Ten days of glorious May sunshine and not a waverer in the ranks of the strikers: a time of optimism and determination that, presently, was undermined by misgivings. A high-ranking lawyer solemnly warned the strikers' leaders that, in law, they were liable to the utmost farthing of their personal fortunes for damages caused by the strike they had called. Nobody saw fit to question this opinion, nor did the credulous leaders elect to put the matter to the test. The news of the humiliating capitulation left a bitter taste. Defeat ... and victory celebrations in the Savoy Grill.

Marked men were singled out on their return to work: 'There's your cards. Services not required.' And gaunt Jack Lashwood, still on strike with the rest of his brotherhood throughout the coalfields of the land, was to be seen with other local colliers pushing ancient bikes or pulling improvised soap-box vehicles to the slag heaps where they did their coal-getting above ground. They poked about in craters, then, from door to door, hawked the fruits of their labours for the meagre benefit of their Mother Hubbard cupboards.

'It sticks in your craw,' James Moleyns said, bitterly. 'Makes me ashamed of the movement. A bloody betrayal, that's what it is.' And, as though to rub it in, Jack Lashwood and all in the coalfields stuck it out, through the summer and autumn, until winter and starvation drove all the miners back to work on the owners' terms.

Long before this we, of Battersby's, began to feel the

effects of the chill winds of economic contraction blowing through the Welsh mining valleys. Orders from these had made up a large part of the volume of our trade. Our glum-faced travellers returned from the villages and towns, not with orders, but requests for postponements in the settlement of accounts. Instead of the customary orders for a dozen of this or that, these fell to half a dozen, a quarter and then, in desperation ...

'Look at this,' Tom Besant said, going through the orders come by post. It was an order from an old and valued customer in Rhondda: '1/12th dozen mohair slip mats, per post.'

'My God!' he went on. 'Pathetic. How's it going to end?'

Answer to this question was indicated by Duckworth's misfortune. Whether it was because of his prolonged diet of 'flag hash', his strenuous exertions wrestling with heavy rolls of linoleum and his habit of economizing by walking to and from work in all weathers I do not know. The fact is that pneumonia took hold of him, reduced him to skeletonic proportions, and, on recovery, not being up to his old job, he had to be given lighter work in another department. The state of trade being as it was he was not replaced, his duties being shared by Tom Besant and me.

We were not paid extra for these services.

# 31

# Feeling the Draught

It is the fashion of this world when an unpleasant fact needs to be stated, to dress it in long-winded words. The word 'retrenchment' was trumpeted about; the victims of its application knew it as 'the sack'.

Messrs Battersby, in company with other firms which felt the draught of the contraction of commerce, merged some of their departments, and those of us who were declared surplus to requirement exchanged our status as Gentlemen for membership of the growing brotherhood of the dole.

By my going, Messrs Battersby saved my twenty-eight shillings a week wages. By attending, twice weekly, a crumbling building that once had been a Reformatory School for erring boys and which now had been taken over by the Ministry of Labour, I was given eighteen shillings weekly for autographing a declaration that I was 'capable of and available for work'.

This severe cut in income meant retrenchment for us at home. Although the old custom was slowly dying there still were many young men and women who 'tipped up the wages' to their parents and received 'spends' in exchange plus their food, clothing and shelter. The usual 'spends' for a young man who was 'signing on' was sixpence or a shilling. If he were keeping the company of a girl or girls there was a universal and necessary understanding that the young lady or ladies paid for their own seats at halls of entertainment and shared the cost of any refreshment. Practical Lotharios who did not wish their darlings to nurse expectations of chivalrous self-denial said, 'I'll meet you inside, love. Save me a seat.'

To me the leisure which unemployment provided was anything but disagreeable. It brought a bubbling sense of freedom at first, a secret elation in being at liberty to indulge in a feast of uninterrupted reading at home, the public library or in those Manchester bookshops where, by tacit consent, the kindly proprietors permitted young men and students to browse among the new books. There was the other motive, the ambition I had been nursing quietly for some time, to try my hand at earning a living from writing. Not that I would have to earn much from this to balance with what I had earned up to now from uncongenial jobs. At their best these had paid no more than twenty-eight shillings a week, at their worst—the less said the better.

There were, in addition, the demands made on my leisure by the dynamic James Moleyns. Not content with acting as lecturer on economics and social history at evening classes at our local Labour Party's headquarters, he persuaded the committee to let him produce a duplicated weekly newspaper. 'There's a job for you,' he said, briskly, when we were together at H.Q. 'Typing. There's the stencils and', giving me some closely written foolscap sheets, 'here's my pieces.' He wrinkled his face and scratched under his chin. 'Aye, and we don't want it to be all tub-thumping. Bit of variety, that's what's needed. Humorous column. Try your hand at that. The kind of people we meet when we're canvassing. Oh, aye, and items of local historical interest. We never see what's under our noses. Friedrich Engels's house in Quay Street; the site of Peterloo. Oh, and Agecroft Hall. They're pulling it down. A Tudor mansion being shipped to America.' His expression changed to one that was almost a glare as he looked at me. 'And all those seven-year-old children from London, fodder for Douglas's cotton mills down Whit Lane. Never seen where they were lodged, have you? Come on, then, before that's pulled down too, and give yourself an eyeful of the good old days a hundred years ago.'

Clumping footfalls sounded in the uncarpeted entrance hall

as we moved to go: Mickmac and Alfie both looking down in the dumps. Mickmac had a length of leather pulley belting coiled round his forearm. He sat on the edge of the table and dropped the belting at his side. 'Fed up,' he said. 'Fed up to the blooming teeth.'

'What's up now?' James asked.

'We asked Nobby to give us a job,' Alfie said, then shrugged.

Mickmac delved into his pocket, took out a battered tin and offered us a choice of his cigarette ends. When we declined he lit one and exhaled on a heavy sigh. 'An' he ticked us off, didn't he, Alfie? Aye, "Don't call me Nobby. Mr Clarke, that's me." ' Mickmac held out an appealing hand. 'I mean —. Well, we all growed up together, didn't we? But he said, "There's no friendship in business." I mean —. Well, it wasn't as though we wus asking for a foreman's job. Labourin'. Anythin' just temporary would ha' done till we've enough stamps on our cards agen.' He looked at James. 'We're run out o' dole benefit.'

'Then go and see Dr Macaulay, the pair o' you.'

Alfie looked at him, puzzled: 'But ... There's nowt ails us.'

'No?' James retorted. 'If I know anything about Doc Macaulay he'll find you're suffering from the complaint called "debility". That's what he'll write on your sick notes, then the pair of you can draw sick benefit. My Christ,' he said, shaking his head, ' "work or full maintenance" eh? Of course, what the Government ought to do is freeze us solid, shove us in cold storage and bring us out when they need us.'

Mickmac's thoughts were still on Nobby. It was as though he had not been listening. He repeated, with murmured incredulity, ' "Mister Clarke, that's me," though. Ticking us off, like that.'

'Well, don't forget he's a big man now,' James said, but the sarcasm was lost.

'I know,' Alfie said. 'Got an accountant, he said, and a good lawyer. Joined the Masons, he has, and set his ma up in a boarding-house in Blackpool. He knows his way around. Just like it in the army, he was. Up to all the tricks.'

James grinned. 'Don't forget to vote for him when he stands for Parliament.'

'In a pig's eye, I will,' Mickmac said and ground the fag end savagely under his heel. His expression changed; he indicated the belting. 'I got this gave me, Jim. Will you mend me boots?'

'Course. We're off for a walk. Coming?'

'Where to?'

'Down Whit Lane and on to Agecroft. They're pulling the old hall down. Shipping it off to America. Something you'll be able to tell your children about. The house that emigrated.'

'Canada,' Alfie murmured.

'America,' James corrected him.

'No,' Alfie replied. 'I mean me. That's where I'm thinking of goin'. Those posters in the dole office. Says you can emigrate there. What's the use of hangin' on here? Fed up, I am, bein' out o' work. Nobody'll gie me a job now I've served me time and want full pay.'

'Been hangin' around outside o' the Motor Works for weeks, me,' Mickmac said. 'There's a crowd always there in Trafford Park waitin' for somebody to get sacked. They're all on the same pay there even if you're only doin' the sweepin' up.' His voice took on a tone of awe. 'Two and six an hour.' He was staring. 'Can you believe it! A quid a day. Five pounds ten a week!'

'My God!' James murmured. ' "Are you capable of and available for work?" What a laugh that is.'

'Well, I don't think five pounds ten a week's owt to laugh at,' Mickmac said.

'Come on, let's get walking,' James said. 'Peckers up. Never say die.'

# 32

# 'He Is Coming'

'You a touch typist?' The dole clerk's tone was abrupt.

I said 'Yes,' without knowing what 'touch typist' meant.

He wrote my name and reference number on a green card. 'There you are. Motor Works. Trafford Park,' he said, adding, warningly, 'It's temporary.'

The Park's twelve hundred acres had, until just before the turn of the century, been the pleasure grounds of the de Trafford mansion house. It and other estates for miles around had been in the uninterrupted ownership and occupation of the de Traffords for eight centuries. A place of woods, plantations and farms with pleasing names. 'Warren Wood', 'Throstle Nest Plantation', 'Waters Meeting Farm'. Stands of oak, beech, chestnut, birch and sycamore through which wild deer roamed and where pheasants roosted.

Young men, a few years older than me, trespassed here when boys to snare rabbits. Its death knell sounded in the closing decades of Victoria's reign when 'Manchester Men' audaciously built the Manchester Ship Canal to break the 'Liverpool Gentlemen's' monopoly in the shipping line. This having been accomplished, ocean-going liners from the seven seas began to sail along the canal past the Park's northern meadows. The de Trafford family sold out. Then the poaching boys in their excursions watched the great trees come crashing down and heard the last gunshots of sportsmen after game. There then descended swarms of workmen to make the desolation complete.

Farewell, woodland ways and singing birds: no more the cock pheasant's challenging cry and the wood pigeon's crooing call; instead, a nightmare transformation. Horrid edifices, reeking temples to the gods of the machine all rearing their monstrous bulks and, from their towering chimneys, brazenly flaunting their black and bulging banners across the sky.

The small area of workmen's houses in the transformed Park were called 'Avenues' as were most of the other industrial roads, and they were named by number, 'First', 'Second' etc., American fashion. When an employee of the Motor Works passed through the works' gates to the clocking-on machines he stepped from Britain into Detroit where Moloch, in the shape of the Main Line Assembly, held unrelenting sway.

Parallel tracks down the central aisle of the main shop's length crept forward at a pre-set pace. Tributary feeder tracks at angles conveniently placed and moving at synchronized speed delivered the prefabricated bits and pieces to the servitors who had to be at their stations along the lines the moment the klaxon blared its imperious and ear-lacerating dissonance. And there the workers stayed, each performing his repetitive operation, until the hooter screamed again signalling the half-hour midday break and the mad rush into the street, rain or shine, to bolt a boxed lunch and devour a cigarette before the siren's discord recalled the hirelings to the paralysing monotony of the endless afternoon. A place where laughter and merry banter were never heard.

The papers that came to us in the drawing office for re-typing were headed 'Eng., Inf.' This engineering information consisted largely of revised specifications of component parts. Each vehicle in the catalogue was anatomized down to its smallest screw, a drawing made of every part and its dimensions minutely described and numbered. These were put away in long rows of filing cabinets so cunningly arranged as to place the filing clerks perpetually under the watchful eye of the office manager on his raised desk.

There were other watchful eyes, men known as 'Spot the Ball', who had roving commissions to trail anybody who was not to be seen at the post of duty or who might be exchanging a time-wasting joke with a fellow worker. The only authorized place where an absentee could be was the privy, and since not one of the long line of these had a door, Spot the Ball could see whether the quarry was taking advantage of privilege by smoking and reading his newspaper.

Managerial policy held organized trades unionism in double contempt, first by not recognizing it, and secondly by paying wages considerably in excess of official rates. The attractive pay was fixed not by the day or week but by the hour, an arrangement convenient to the company's thrifty policy should its supply of components break down. When this occurred, all who were held up until the interrupted flow was made good heard the foreman's abrupt command. 'Okay, you men. Clock off. All outside.' The time-recording clocks began to 'Ping—ping-ping' and the temporarily unemployed trooped into the street to join the permanent group of eager optimists known as 'the Band of Hope' standing there waiting to take the place of any unfortunate whom Spot the Ball had fired.

'Rotten hole. Rotten, lousy, stinkin' hole.' The speaker, Sandy Sinclair, was a middle-aged, bald, spectacled and pot-bellied man in charge of the A to E section of the filing cabinets and he nursed a bitter grudge against fortune which had, up to now, frustrated his dearest ambition. During those parts of the day when his revulsion against his servitude reached bursting point, he poured out to me all his pent-up emotion when appearing at my desk with typing orders: 'Look at me,' he muttered, speaking out of the side of his mouth, eyes for ever on the watch for our common prowling enemy or the office manager's wandering glance. 'Look at me. Stuck in here, all for the want of a miserable hundred quid. If I was single it'd be—oh, well, I'm wed and there's the family. But—once let me get that hundred quid and you'll see me, out there in God's fresh air. A big satchel here', he patted his belly, 'and *this* written on it. Here, give us your scribblin' pad.' He wrote on this, in block letters:

SANDY SINCLAIR
THE OLD FIRM

'Yes,' a huge sigh, 'a hundred measly quid and I'll be out of here like a bat out of hell. Can you see me?' He took a deep breath, put his hand to the side of his mouth and, in suppressed tones, cried: 'Six to four the fieeeld.' Then, seeing the manager glancing our way, retired busily with his papers to the cabinets.

He buttonholed me in the street during lunch break to enlarge on the intensity of his agony. 'Only one ten to one chance, that's all I need.' His tone was cringing and pleading as though he was convinced that the gods had given me full power to grant or withhold from him his heart's desire. 'I tell you, ten quid on a winning ten to one chance. A hundred quid', he held out his palm, 'in there.' He clenched his fist suddenly on the imagined money. 'Aye,' he said, with a vicious smile and burning eyes, 'then *I*'d be the bookie.' The glorious dream was brief. His hand fell slowly to his side and all the eagerness left his countenance as he confessed lamely, 'But I'm a fool. A bloody fool. Well, look at me, *placing* bets instead of taking 'em. Every night I'm at the dog tracks an' I keep tellin' myself, "You *can't* win, unless you're the bookie." ' He looked at me challengingly as though expecting contradiction. 'Havn' I proved it? Doesn' it stand to sense?' He then turned with a snarling expression of bitter hatred to stare at the temple of mass production at our backs. 'Stinkin', rotten, lousy, bastard hole. But just let me get my maulers on a hundred quid … '

Mickmac, who had detached himself from the Band of Hope to join us, said, fervently: 'Stinkin' rotten hole, eh?'

Well, I wish they'd gie me a start. *I*'d do anythin' to get took on. Anythin'.'

Sandy threw him a sour, unsympathetic look. 'Then you keep on stickin' around. I'll lay you any money you like they'll be firin' 'em by the dozen next week. *He*'s coming.'

'He' was the Great Mogul himself, enthroned thousands of miles away in the land of the free. Those who were his managerial watchdogs trembled when, from afar, came rumours that a sudden visit from Him was imminent and this nervousness affected all the underlings of our branch of His far-flung empire. When the threatened descent did not materialize the rank and file muttered that this cry of 'Wolf' was a ruse to keep the watchdogs on the snap and snarl.

This time, though, all doubt was banished. He *was* on his way. All the newspapers carried photographs of Him stepping aboard a transatlantic liner, the King of Mass Production accompanied by his Baronage, the Heads of Departments. Big men, tough men who had bulldozed their way to power and who held on to it by the exercise of un-remitting ruthlessness. King and Barons alike, the news-papers said on their arrival, were come to see the company's vast new works now in process of completion on the Thames's lower reaches.

All in the Manchester works, which now was to be super-seded, were on tenterhooks. Works and office managers, taut and sweating, communicating their irritability to under-managers, foremen and Spot the Ball who, in turn, took it out on the lower deck. When would He come? No sign, no news, a prolonged and charged expectancy until all felt like prisoners in the dock waiting the tardy reappearance of the jury.

In the event Himself disdained visiting his Lancastrian territory. In His place a Baron, armed with full authority, was dispatched to examine the personnel eligible and worthy of transfer to the South.

Absolute power, being a bully, attracts its like. He who came in place of Him wore the purple with brute arrogance. Of Scandinavian extraction, he was oversized, ham-fisted and excessively muscular. His contemptuous, transatlantic nasal bellowings had our intimidated superiors on the skip and jump, though not all employees of low degree were impressed. On his progress through the main line assembly shop the Ambassador, making a random selection from the workmen, picked on the wrong man with the question, 'Say. You. Would you work harder if you were paid more?'

'I suppose so,' the man said, unsuspectingly.

'Fire him,' the Ambassador said to his aide, then received a lesson in the danger of pushing a man too far: he was sent on his back, spitting teeth and blood. The sacked man flung aside the twelve-inch monkey wrench and, without further parley, made for the main gates and the dole queue, a familiar path so many of us were soon to tread once again.

# 33

# A Fall from Grace

Our parish church of Pendleton occupies the place of honour on Broad Street, the local section of the main highway from Manchester to the North. Along the street's length and in some of the side streets running at right angles from it are churches and chapels of every denomination of the Anglican heresy. Up to the outbreak of World War I both parish church and all those of the nonconformist persuasion had their free and rented pews well filled with worshippers every Sabbath. The threadbare years of peace that followed victory's ghastly slaughter saw a great falling-off in religious ardour and, here and there, as congregations dwindled to insignificant proportions, sacred property was disposed of to the profanity of commerce. Some became movie flea-pits, others waterproof garment manufactories and one, a branch of the municipal library.

Here, in the warmth of the seedy reading-room, the shabby unemployed, young and old, filled in the tedium of the passing days. The notice said SILENCE, but men coughed, hawked, blew their noses, wheezed and sometimes snored until awakened by a prod from a neighbour. To discourage gamblers the newspapers' racing columns were either cut out or obliterated—to no avail. Devotees of the kingly sport smuggled in the racing editions and, in whispered conference, whilst one of their number kept watch, decided on their fancy and contributed their halfpenny or penny to a syndicate. Others whose empty pockets banished all hope of favours from the girls, waited their turn to look at the *Illustrated London News*. Here, in a centre page double spread, an R.A. staff artist weekly depicted a Bacchanalian scene from ancient Rome and elsewhere, the foreground dominated by disturbingly beautiful young women in all their lovely nakedness, standing or reclining in seductive poses.

On waist-high sloping desks fitted to the walls the newspapers' 'Situations Vacant' pages were pinned and here down-at-heel clerks, salesmen, commercial travellers and others wrote down the box numbers and particulars of whatever jobs were being offered: ' ... state age, experience and wages required in own handwriting.'

'Dear Sirs,
    With reference to your advertisement under Box number ...
    My qualifications are several years' experience as salesman, double-entry book-keeping and typing. I am quick and accurate at figures and am capable of dealing with correspondence. I have satisfactory testimonials, am twenty-six years of age and suggest a wage of...'

Thirty shillings? Don't be daft. What of those tales of men with university degrees being glad to land a job selling vacuum cleaners door-to-door on commission? Twenty-five shillings? Can't go much lower than that what with tram fares and dinner money. Still—. Don't forget, unless you get some new stamps on your card soon—. Play safe, man. Ask twenty-two and six. After all, you could walk to work and back and save the tram fares and there'd always be the chance of a rise in pay later on.

A letter in response to one of these applications came from a Manchester firm of 'Estate and Business Transfer Agents and Valuers', asking me to call at Suite 39, third floor, in a newly erected building not far from Messrs Battersby's establishment. I was to be interviewed by the junior partner. The letter's heading was impressively die-stamped and it also gave the address of the firm's other office in Birmingham and added, cryptically ' ... and London'.

The junior partner was a fat, thick-lipped young man whose

black, kinky hair, parted in the middle, was heavily bril-
liantined and constantly being combed—that is, when he was
not at work with a manicure set or grimacing at his reflection
in a collapsible shaving mirror while removing blackheads
from nose, cheeks and jowl.

Suite 39 consisted of a room which had been divided into
two, the junior partner's being the one at the back. The front
was furnished with a filing cabinet, typist's table and chair and
another small table and chair. There was a counter with a
flap and door below. The bareness of the walls was relieved
by framed advertisements of insurance companies and
building societies for which the firm was agent.

I was interrogated closely. The junior partner's enjoyment
of his authority was such that the interview was prolonged. My
answers satisfied him and he decided that I would fill the bill.
He then told me that this branch was newly opened and, as to
wages, the company would offer me twenty shillings a week
' ... as a start, then we'll see how you go on. It's a very good
chance for you to learn the business. Well?'

I accepted.

My new employer nodded. 'Right. Start on Monday—
with the typist,' he said, adding, 'Oh, call me Mister Cecil.
My brother's Mister Archie. He's the Birmingham end.'

The business was simplicity itself. The newspapers'
'Businesses and Houses For Sale & Wanted' columns provided
the merchandise. My first instruction was to comb the
columns of those for sale, paying particular attention to any
businesses which advertised 'ill health cause of sale' and
making notes of the box numbers of any which also said 'No
agents'. I then was required to write a lying letter, not on the
firm's notepaper, but on a blank sheet addressed from my
home. In this I expressed interest and asked for full details.
The anxious seller revealed the address and was visited by
Mr Cecil in his baby Austin car and me, as secretary, in
attendance.

He greeted the vendor effusively, told him that he had heard the business was for sale and assured him that the company had commissions by the dozen from people who were in the market for suitable businesses. 'I think,' he said, while the vendor was reading the company's business card, 'I think,' Mr Cecil said, as he appraised the place, 'I think this would be just the thing for Mrs Yates—or Mr Benson.' He rang the changes on these and other fictitious names. 'Yes, just the thing.' He went outside, inspected the shop front and looked up and down the street, then re-entered as one now satisfied. 'Good position. Needs a bit of modernizing. You might have to bring your price down a few pounds. You'd consider a reasonable offer, I suppose—er—stock at valuation, of course?'

The ill health pleaded by the vendors was, almost invariably, a state of consuming anxiety which could only be cured when the near-bankrupt business was somebody else's responsibility. The effect of the mention of Mrs Yates and Mr Benson was immediate. Lips were moistened and eyes brightened with hope, then, after further patter, and when Mr Cecil judged the time to be ripe, he said, 'Yes? Right. Very well,' and turned to me. 'Advise Mrs Yates and Mr Benson.' A glance at the vendor. 'All right for them to call without appointment?' This having been agreed he said, as an afterthought, 'Oh, yes,' a smile, 'we'll need the sole agency, of course. Right?' To me, snapping finger and thumb while speaking, 'Particulars and form of agreement.' I produced the closely printed foolscap form and filled in the details. Afterwards Mr Cecil took the contract from me to check, mumbling, as he read, all I had written. 'Right. That's it. Telephone all the particulars to the Birmingham office. Lend him your pen. Just sign there and we'll get moving straight away.'

Prospective buyers were lured to the office by a glowing advertisement offering, at bargain price, an old-established and prosperous family business, 'bereavement sole cause of sale'. When callers arrived Mr Cecil was full of apology that the bargain had been sold. 'Went just like that.' He snapped his fingers and, having assessed the visitor's credulity, enthusiastically got to grips with the formidable task of trying to pull off a sale in a buyers' market.

Vendors who had been waiting for Mrs Yates and Mr Benson appeared at the office from time to time. Their expressions of querulous anxiety were matched with Mr Cecil's look of surprise. 'Not *been*? What, neither of them?'

'No. No sign at all. An' I've never been out. An'—er—well, from what you said about 'em an', you know, me bein' willin' to bring the price down reasonable—I mean to say, it's only run down because of my health. Only wants buildin' up, that's all. I mean—well, I ask you. By rights I ought to be in hospital.'

He was comforted with further lies and, when he had departed, I was instructed to tell him or her, the next time they called, that Mr Cecil was away at the Birmingham office.

Our frustrated clients were not alone in their need for comfort. In late autumn Mr Cecil arrived flushed, flustered and staring. He carried *The Financial Times* which, in company with other newspapers, announced a stupendous crash of stocks and shares on Wall Street. 'Birmingham,' he said: 'Get me Birmingham,' then blundered into his office. His voice could be heard, low and strained at first, as he conferred with Mr Archie; it then developed a sack-cloth and ashes volubility when the dire consequences of rash speculation were discussed in all their hopeless detail. For a few weeks his bounce and self-assurance were submerged by a subdued preoccupation which changed its form into an edgy irritability and a policy of all-round economy. The typist was given notice. I took over her duties without extra pay. Three weeks before Christmas Mr Cecil did not appear on pay day. The following Monday when I asked for my dues he said, with a backhand wave and keeping his eyes down, 'Oh, pay you this week-end.'

My mother said, 'All right, lad,' when I explained why my weekly contribution to the exchequer was not forthcoming and, without further comment, my customary half-crown spending money was advanced.

Instead of two weeks' wages the following pay-day Mr Cecil said, 'Waiting for Mr Archie to countersign the cheque. Back from London next Wednesday. Three weeks' pay in time for Christmas.'

When she came home from work that night Mother looked at me. 'Is there anything, lad?' she asked. The hope in her voice was galling.

Christmas Eve. By late afternoon it was clear that neither Mr Cecil nor Mr Archie was going to show up.

Christmas—and skint. What could I do about it?

I went round the corner to Messrs Battersby's packing and forwarding department where an old acquaintance gave me a couple of large sheets of brown paper and some string. As the Manchester Town Hall clock struck the hour which brought the business of the day to an end I retrieved my unstamped insurance cards, made a parcel of the typewriter, took it outside, locked the office door and put the key through the letter box, then lugged my stolen burden home.

# 34

# 'Hard Cases . . .'

Knowing what a stickler for honesty Mother was I put the typewriter in my bedroom, picked up the Christmas cards the postman had pushed under the door, lit the fire, made tea and waited.

Mother would not be home until after seven, my sister, now a counter clerk in the post office, not until after eight. Some kids were going from door to door carol singing. They stopped at ours.

> 'God rest you merry, gentlemen
> Let nothing you dismay ... '

There were three halfpence on the mantelpiece, change from something or other. I gave the kids a halfpenny and was wished a merry Christmas.

'Let nothing you dismay.' Christmas — out of work and skint, tasting afresh what had been Alfie's and Mickmac's lot for months, though I recalled their envy of my being able to get a job of sorts.

> Dear Sirs,
>     In answer to your advertisement. I am twenty-six years of age ...

No, I now was twenty-seven. Why! soon I would be thirty. Appalling.

On entering Mother asked the inevitable question, not by words but with a look. My answer caused her to dump 'the bag' on the table and exclaim explosively as she took off hat and coat.

'The villains,' she declared. 'Done out of three weeks' pay—

and Christmas. Well, they're having no more out of you. You aren't going back and that *is* a fact.' I kept quiet. She added, when her indignation had subsided, 'Never mind, lad.' She sat and opened her purse. 'God's good. We didn't do so badly out of the staff Christmas box. Two pounds ten each. What a blessing. Wait,' she interrupted herself, reached for the rent book behind the clock on the mantel, counted out the money and set this and the book on the mantel's edge. 'There. That's that.' She gave me a pound note. 'Bottle of whisky and a bottle of port. Tell them you want a bottle of good port.'

Every Christmas morning our first cup of tea was laced with a teaspoon of whisky, the bottle then being firmly stoppered and put away for medicinal use; the wine, the 'teetotallers' drink', was passed round among visiting friends for Christmas cheer. She emptied the bag. 'Here,' she said, giving it to me, 'put them in there in case of accident—and don't forget to count the change. Oh, and—er—' She opened her purse again, gave me three shillings. 'Bit of spending money. Never say die, lad. And—h'm— Here.' I was given three slim books. *Hamlet*, *Macbeth* and *The Tempest* in Messrs Dent's Temple Shakespeare edition. 'And get those in your noddle.' As I was leaving she called after me: 'Ask Annie Boarder and Polly Mytton to call round for a drink.' I heard the earthenware baking dish being lugged from the cupboard as I walked away.

Polly Mytton and Mrs Boarder were either side the fireplace when I got back. Polly, apron starched and gleaming as white as her snowy hair, sat looking downcast as she stared at the dough set to rise on the fender. Alfie grinned at me from the sofa. Wineglasses and corkscrew were on the table.

'Wherever have you been?' Mother asked and said 'Oh,' when I explained that I had been chatting with James Moleyns.

'Aye,' Mrs Boarder said, sternly, 'and you ought to get him and some of those Labour councillors to summon that firm you've been working for. Three weeks' wages, eh? *And* only three bob a week more than you'd get signing on.'

The cork popped, glasses were filled and distributed. Mrs Boarder raised her glass. 'Well, another year gone by, lass. God bless.'

'And bedamned to trouble and worries,' Mother responded. 'A merry Christmas to us all.'

I noticed Mrs Boarder's smile fade. She was looking at Polly who, with an expression of sad preoccupation, was staring again into the fender quite forgetful of the wine. Mrs Boarder frowned. 'Hey, there. And what's come over thee, Polly?'

Without warning Polly's chin sank on to her chest; tears splashed on the back of her hand.

'Whatever's the matter, lass?' Mother said, concerned.

'He's goin',' Polly answered, in a broken voice.

Alfie shifted uncomfortably, moistened his lips and looked at his boots.

'Going?' Mrs Boarder repeated, contracting her brows. 'Going where?'

Alfie coughed, nervously. 'Got fed up with looking, Mrs Boarder. I did, really. I've been taken for Canada – farmin'.' He went on, in self-defence and as though the confession would be of some consolation to Polly. 'If I could ha' got a job here I wouldn't ha' gone. Sick o' trying.'

'You were neither drag nor burden to me, lad,' Polly said.

'I know that. But –' a shrug, 'you know.'

Eyes still downcast Polly sniffed a couple of times. Mrs Boarder and Mother murmured comfortingly. Polly looked from Mrs Boarder to Mother, her eyes full of bewilderment. 'I don't know what's come over the world. I know there's been out o' work round here often enough ever since I can remember. But now it's all different. Summat's gone wrong.' She looked at Alfie. 'Ay, lad ... ' and she shook her head, lost for words.

'Less o' this, now, Polly,' Mrs Boarder said, roughly. 'One thing's for sure, he's not goin' off soldierin' *this* time. And he can always come back when things buck up agen here. He's

got a trade in his fingers, don't forget. Come thee on, lass, sup
your drink and look on the bright side. And don't forget, we've
all got our tickets for Boxing Night. Aye, I *do* look forward to
my ninepennorth o' pantomime.'

She was interrupted by the excited shouts of children and
the pounding of running footfalls in the street. Mrs Boarder
was at the door immediately. 'The band,' she called to us
excitedly. 'It's the band.' We all joined her. Every front door
was open, each casting its shaft of light on to the pavement.
The Pendleton Silver Prize Band formed a wide circle at the
street junction and filled the air with carols and Christmas
hymns. There was a drift of neighbours to encircle the band;
passers-by joined the attentive crowd waiting for the grand
finale, the ever-favourite tune that brought carousers from the
pubs to swell the throng, the song that opened all hearts and
sent to the sky the full-throated chorus that, for however brief
a time, banished for everybody the worries of the world and
its ways:

'Jerusalem, Jerusalem, lift up your heads and sing,
Hosanna, in the highest ... '

The day after the season of goodwill ended I was alone in the
house when a rat-tat sounded on the front door. Mr Cecil and,
behind him, his baby Austin with engine running.

His eyes were wide; he was affronted and indignant.
'Where's ... ' he began. I interrupted, telling him that it was
safely within and that on receipt of three weeks' wages plus
his contribution to my insurance stamps his property would be
restored. He called me a thief and threatened to drive off to
fetch the police if I did not hand over instantly. I said that I
would not hand over but would await his return.

He came back next morning and persuaded me into the
street to look into the back of his car where lay a typewriter of
such antiquity that it might have been standing forgotten for
years in a remote corner of a scrap-metal merchant's yard.

'Look,' he said, reducing the business to the level appropriate
to a bazaar of the Middle East. 'Look. I'll tell you what I'll
do —' he pointed to the old iron on the back seat, held out his
palm which he slapped suddenly with his other hand. 'That —
and thirty shillings. What d'you say?'

It was not so much a case of what I had to say rather than
Mrs Boarder who, listening to the conversation, not only
joined in but took complete charge. Pointing a finger at Mr
Cecil and fixing him with a glittering eye she, as though
giving a demonstration to a class of student Town Criers,
bawled, '*Oho!*' Neighbours hurried to their doors as her war
cry resounded through the street: '*Oho!* So! *You're* the feller
that doesn't pay the wages, eh? Live on air, is it?' The neighbours joined her, among them being Mrs Flarty with her
sweeping brush. All began to make hostile noises. 'We know
where we stand with the bloody pawnbroker,' Mrs Boarder
continued menacingly. 'We know where we stand with the
bloody pawnbroker, the soddin' rent man and all them that
come round for the weekly payments. But *you*, you're like my
arse, the best out of sight. And listen, you fat-gutted, pimply-
faced, half-got get.' She gave him a push that sent him back a
couple of paces. 'Gerrout. Buzz. Shunt — and if you have the
sauce to show that ugly dial of yours round here again, by the
livin' Jesus I'll ... ' as she was speaking she raised her muscular
right arm and reached down the back of her neck as though to
scratch an inaccessible itch. In his eagerness to dive for the
safety of his car Mr Cecil accidently trod on Mrs Boarder's
carpet-slippered foot. 'Did it a-purpose,' she shouted and
snatched at Mrs Flarty's brush and brought it down like a
sledge hammer on the car's roof. It made a deep dent and the
brush handle shattered. 'Me brush!' Mrs Flarty protested, but
Mr Cecil did not hear anything of the ensuing altercation. His
car disappeared in a cloud of exhaust and nothing was seen or
heard of him again.

# 35

# 'What Can You Do?'

A brisk knock on our door. My hopeful expectation was dispelled the instant the postman handed me a bulky foolscap envelope. The publisher's letter clipped to the novel's cover was terse. It regretted that my offering was not suitable for inclusion in his list and it also served as reminder that the way ahead was to be long, hard and discouraging with no guarantee of ultimate success. This, in turn, opened the door to gloomy thoughts and projected a future wherein I and all like me were to be superfluous for ever and ever.

We had seen the election of a Labour Government at Westminster which, we had hoped, would set the wheels of industry turning once again. Unfortunately Labour had but twenty-six more seats than the Conservatives, a precarious balance which, at any time, could be upset if the Liberals decided to cast their fifty-nine votes with the Opposition. I put the rejected manuscript aside. Dwelling on this and the political stalemate was futile. Try something else. What about short stories? Out of nowhere came the recollection of Sandy Sinclair and his consuming hatred of the Motor Works' factory environment. What had happened to him? What could have happened? In his way was he not like me basically, in pursuit of the same thing, searching, like so many, for a way out of intolerable conditions? His desire was to make a book, mine to write one. 'A Maker of Books.' There's the title, anyway. All that I had to do now was to write the story.

I sat down again and looked at the stencil in the typewriter. It was a piece James Moleyns had written for the local party's duplicated news sheet. It was in answer to a leader in the *Manchester Guardian* on 'Unemployment' from which he had

extracted a quotation: ' ... for we, the English nation, are
the heirs of a century of prosperity ... ' I picked up at that
point where the postman had interrupted.

> Prosperity for whom? What proportion of it came or is
> coming the way of those whose labours produced it?
> Indeed, and without reference to J.L. and Barbara
> Hammond's books on social and industrial history, the
> writer of the leader need only walk a couple of miles in
> any direction from the *Manchester Guardian*'s office and
> see for himself the insulting living conditions which the
> majority of his fellow men and all who went before have
> had to endure over the past, prosperous century. Every
> week that passes sees the queues growing longer at the
> dole offices. The men and women for whom work cannot
> be found are heirs indeed. There are two million of them,
> all 'capable of and available for work', their skills rust-
> ing, their physique going to waste because that self-
> perpetuating and unholy trinity, Rent, Interest and
> Profit, must extort its pound of flesh before the needs of
> common humanity are served ...

I stopped to listen as I heard a sudden commotion in the
street. Through the window I saw Polly Mytton standing on
her doorstep in the company of three or four neighbours.
She was beaming with excitement as she showed them a newspaper which she held open in both hands. Mrs Boarder came
round the corner, her shawl draped loosely over her shoulders,
her left hand holding her purse and a thick wad of pawntickets. The breeze was blowing her hair about and I noticed,
for the first time, how grey this was become. Though she still
carried herself erect there was the hint of a plod in her gait.

Curiosity took me outside as Mrs Boarder joined the group.
'Look, Annie, look,' Polly exclaimed excitedly. 'It's from
Alfie. Postman's just brought it. Eee! Fancy, now! Havin' his
photo in the paper!'

It was a Canadian dock-side scene. The photographer had collected a number of immigrants of Alfie's size and grouped them around a towering North-West Mountie. All were grinning. The caption said, 'The Cream of England Arrives.'

'You see,' Mrs Boarder said. 'He got there safe, you and all your worritin'. And all that money they've got over there. For all you know he might end up a millionaire and invite you over for a holiday.'

The women laughed, then all looked at Mickmac who had joined us. He carried a book of printed tickets perforated at the stub. 'Anybody want to buy one?' he asked and added, ingratiatingly, 'On'y a shillin' each.'

'A *shil*lin'?' Mrs Boarder repeated, scoffingly. 'You've got some hopes. A shillin'!' she went on, looking at her companions. 'As though anybody's got shillin's for raffles.'

'It isn't a raffle,' Mickmac protested. 'They *give* you things if you sell a bookful.'

'Who gives you things—and what?' Mrs Boarder said, suspiciously.

'Look. See for yourself,' Mickmac assured her, proffering the book. 'Great Universal Stores. Sell twenty tickets, take the money and all the names you've wrote down and you can have a quid's worth of anything you want, *free*. Boots, beddin', clothes, crockery. Ooo! Their place is jam-packed full o' things you can choose from.'

'Aye?' Mrs Boarder replied, unimpressed. 'And what do them as buys the tickets get for their shillin's?'

'Why, a book o' tickets, o' course. They send all who've wrote their names down a book o' tickets. All you've to do is sell 'em, then you can have what *you* want.'

'Oh aye? Then let me tell you this, Mick McBride, no Great Universal Stores is getting any shillin's o' mine and that *is* for certain.' She frowned at Polly Mytton. 'And you can put that purse o' yours away, Polly. You've quite enough to do wi' your pennies.' She took her and those neighbours for whom she had been to the pawnshop to her home for settlement.

'Mind her own business, that's what Annie Boarder ought to do,' Mickmac said, savagely. 'She'd ha' bought one, would Polly Mytton. Me mam's dependin' on me sellin' this lot so's she can get summat to pawn.' His expression changed to one of dolour. 'Nowt's goin' right,' he mumbled. He continued, eyes downcast, when I asked what else had gone wrong: 'Given me the door, she has. Railway fireman, that's who she's hooked up wi' now. Aye, he'll never be out o' work.' He looked at me defiantly after a little pause. 'But I don't care.' Then the hand holding the tickets fell to his side. Once again he looked at the pavement and said, in the tones of one who might have been talking to himself, 'Wish they'd have taken me for Canada with Alfie. Told me it's no use if you haven't got a trade.' He sighed. 'Dog bite me! What can you do?'

MY MATERNAL GRANDPARENTS,
MY SISTER AND ME

# 36

# Postman's Knock

My discouraging and growing pile of rejected manuscripts had one positive quality — the undeniable proof of practice. The regrets that each brought from the Editors, while momentarily disheartening, did not deter. Hope's tiny gleam, though it burned very low betimes, was never entirely extinguished. Patience. Keep at it. One of these days ...

The postman's time of arrival could be anything between nine and half past. My sister had to be at work before this. Mother did not leave for the café until around the nine fifteen mark, though sometimes she dallied the minutes away over this and that, then had to leave in a rush. While awaiting the postman's call I liked to have the house to myself. My pride, hope, ambition — call it what you will — preferred not to have a witness on the scene when it was injured. There the situation was, silence in the street, the minutes ticking away, Mother fussing as she prepared to leave while I, striving to hide my impatient irritability, strained my ears for the postman's footfalls.

'Now, let me see. There's the bag. Oh, lord! Where's my purse! Have you seen my purse, lad?'

'Don't tell me you've lost that again, Mother.'

I was corrected: 'It is not lost. It is mislaid. And look at the time!' She hadn't any regular hiding-place and, as she usually put the purse away last thing of a night when she was a-weary, it was not to be wondered that, sometimes, she could not recall its place of concealment. On this occasion I found it stuffed at the back of one of the drawers of the sewing-machine.

'There! I knew it wasn't very far away,' she said and gave me sixpence. 'Give it to Polly Mytton for me, lad. It's towards

Mrs Dacre's wreath. Explain how it is to Katie Harrington. I'd have gone to the service if I could. Go in my place, there's a lad. And see you're at the café before the rush sets in.'

The injunction referred to the arrangement she had made with the café's management committee whereby she paid for my meal and I, as a non-member, was permitted to lunch provided I put in an appearance in advance of the general arrival. 'The walk there and back will do you good and I'll be certain you've had a meal.' There was another advantage. Adjoining the restaurant was a reading-room whose tables carried all the daily papers, literary reviews, supplements, illustrated weeklies and monthly magazines.

She went off in a hurry muttering, 'My goodness. Just look at the time! I'll have to put my best foot forward.' I followed her to the door. No sign of the postman. Perhaps he had passed by our street. With most in the neighbourhood letters were rare. When one was delivered it often caused a flurry of excitement or apprehension. I saw him turning the corner and I withdrew into the house, leaving the door ajar as I listened to his footsteps. They halted on the street's opposite side and I heard him make his usual 'rat-tat' with his small knobstick. I glanced through the window: Mrs Boarder was opening her door to him. He gave her a letter and walked on.

Mrs Boarder did not move from her step. She was looking at the envelope. After a little hesitation she broke the seal, read the letter, glanced at our open front door and came across.

'Are you there, lad?' She came in, frowning heavily. 'Just read that,' she said and sat. The letter was headed from a Newcastle-on-Tyne address. 'First time I've heard from our Hetty in a year and more, the faggot.'

I read:

Dear Mam,
    Can you lend me the fare home? I've been meaning

to write for months but you know how things are
when you're always on the move. It's this radio that's
half the trouble. They're all sitting at home listening-in
that's why business is so terrible. I'll pay you back when
I get a job. Charlie's going to send me something if the
act goes down well in America. So I will close now hoping
this finds you in the pink.

Your loveing daughter,

HETTY

P.S. The baby's no trouble at all.

I looked at her, she at me. 'Yes,' she said, 'you've need to
look. A baby, is it? An' who's bloody Charlie, that's what I
want to know. Aye, and what's he done? Sodded off to
America. My Christ, if it's not one thing it's another.' She
sighed heavily, shook her head and said: 'The fare she wants.
An' what's that going to cost? Have you any idea, lad?'

'I'll let you know when I get back from town,' I said and
passed her the letter. She looked at it and shook her head.
'What am I going to find to pawn for her fare? "P.S. The
baby's no trouble at all." Ay, aye, oh. Ah well, all we can do
is make the poor little bugger welcome.' She rose to go as a
voice at the door said, 'I'm comin' in. It's only me.' Polly
Mytton. Her snowy hair save for a tiny fringe was quite concealed by an old-fashioned, close-fitting bonnet decorated
with black sequins. She carried a prayer and hymn book
whose ivory binding contrasted conspicuously with her black
gloves and dark dress. 'You'd better hurry if you're coming,
Annie,' she said. 'The hearse and carriages're turning the corner. We ought to be in church before they come, you know.'

'Stop your mitherin', woman,' Mrs Boarder said. 'We'll be
there.'

Polly noticed the letter in Mrs Boarder's hand. Her
expression changed. 'Is owt wrong, lass?' She was told. 'Ay,'
she said, astonished. 'I didn't know Hetty was wed.'

'I don't know whether she is, either,' Mrs Boarder
answered. 'Er—er—' a touch of ingratiation came to her
voice. 'Lend us your weddin' ring, Polly. It's for her fare. I'll
get it back for you out o' pawn.'

'O' course I will, you silly madam.'

The hearse and a couple of black cars stopped outside Mrs
Dacre's house. Mrs Boarder glanced through the window.
'Ah, well, there'll be an end one day. There's old Bessie
Dacre, past all cares and worries now.'

'Yes,' Polly agreed, then raised her eyebrows in surprise,
'Funny thing about Charlie Dacre. The only thing of his
ma's he wanted was that photo of his dad and Billy Lad
outside the old smithy. Wants his childer to see their grand-
dad. Aye, all the rest that's left he wants Katie Harrington to
have.'

'I should think so, too,' Mrs Boarder commented. 'Him
workin' at Rolls Royce and never known a day's out o' work.
No wonder he's put on all that weight.'

A few days later, walking home from Manchester, I saw
Hetty, child in her arms, getting off a tramcar. The guard
carried her battered suitcase to the pavement and put it on
the kerb. I took the case from her. The smile she gave me was
constrained and this, I guessed, as we walked and chatted,
was caused by her trying to conceal the fact that two of her
upper front teeth were missing. We both behaved with some
awkwardness. For my part I was disturbed by the unexpected change in her appearance since last we had seen
each other—disturbed and saddened that all her bloom was
gone.

Their front door was ajar, her mother not at home. 'Don't
go,' she said after I had put her suitcase down. 'Have a cup of
tea. Here. Hold the baby.' Freed of her burden she took off her
coat and hat, patted her hair and said, with a wry face, as
she looked at the framed early photograph of herself in stage
dress, 'Oh, heck! Don't remind me.' She had put the kettle on

now, and was looking at the milk jug. 'Oh. No milk,' she said, then opened her purse. 'Go and get a pennorth, lad.'

'I'll bring a drop from home,' I said, glad of the opportunity to be relieved of the baby. I had another motive. Had the postman been? He had not. As I came from our house I saw her mother walking down the street. She carried a loaf and a stone jam-jar full of black treacle.

'Oh, she's back, is she?' Mrs Boarder said as I joined her.

Hetty had her child straddled across her hip. Her mother said, on entering, 'You could have let me know the time of your train, couldn't you? I'd have come to meet you.'

'Didn't want to be no bother, Mam.'

'And this Charlie. Who is he?' I saw her glance from Hetty to the baby then back at her daughter again.

'Didn't I send you the programme when Charlie and me first started the double act?'

'Act, is it? And where's your wedding ring?'

'Give over, Ma.'

'Don't you tell me to give over, madam. Where is it?'

'Pawned. I had to have summat to live on when me savings'd gone. Hey!' She stopped and stared, regarding her mother with indignation. 'I'll have you know I'm wed proper.' She pointed to the suitcase. 'In there, me marriage lines are.'

'I should hope they are, too, madam.'

Hetty added, inconsequentially: 'And me teeth came out after he was born.'

Her mother let this pass. 'And what's all that about this here Charlie shootin' off to America?'

'Like I told you. It's the radio. It's killin' the music hall. He's a good comic. Teamed up with another chap and they've got six weeks' contract in the States. He'd've took us with him but—well, you know, it was the fare. Don't worry, he'll be sending us some money if the act goes well.'

'Oh, aye? Well, all contributions gratefully received.' She

put the loaf and jam-jar on the table, threw off her shawl, sat and held out her arms. 'Come on. Let's be havin' him. What's his name?'

'Charlie—and Jack, after me dad.' She added, by way of reassurance, 'Don't worry about our keep, Mam. I'll ask for me job back in the laundry or get summat else.'

Her mother who was smiling at the child in her lap did not appear to be listening. I was. I heard the postman's rat-tat up the street and I began to sidle to the door as the grandmother started to tickle the child. 'Look! He's laughing. Oh! He's a beauty. Ay, he's a little love.' She began to jounce Charlie Jack while singing:

> 'Little lad, little lad where were you born?
> Far off in Lancashire, under a thorn,
> Where they sup buttermilk with a ram's horn;
> And a pumpkin scooped with a yellow rim
> Is the bonny bowl they breakfast in.'

The postman was approaching our door. Would he? Wouldn't he? He stopped, rapped twice, flicked a letter through the open door, then passed on. I excused myself, resisted the temptation to sprint and strolled across. The letter was headed 'The Storyteller Magazine' and was signed by 'The Editor'. I read ' ... and would like to have your story "A Maker of Books" for publication and offer twenty-five guineas for the first British serial rights ... '

Oh, lord!

# 37

# A Let-down

My sister, home from work, read the letter, looked at me in wonderment, then expressed her jubilation in a spontaneous jig on the hearthrug. When Mother arrived she, having listened to my sister's gabbled tale, flopped into her chair, 'the bag' in one hand, her handbag in the other. 'Well, I never!' On my sister's repeating the sum that had been offered Mother looked at me and said, anxiously: 'Do you think the gentleman's made a mistake, lad?'

I laughed and pooh-poohed the suggestion in, I regret to have to confess, a lofty and scornful manner that called down a deserved and instant rebuke. 'There is no occasion for you to let it go to your head, young man. "Pride goeth before a fall," remember.'

'Oh, *Mother*,' my sister interjected, impatiently.

'*Twenty*-five guineas, though,' Mother said, awed, then, with relish, and forgetting the sin for which I had just been ticked off, 'Wait until my regular café customers hear *this*.'

Twenty-six pounds five shillings! A pound a week for half a year. A pound, the equivalent of wages for a week's work at detestable clerking and two shillings a week more than unemployment pay, not to mention the delight of so congenial an occupation. It needed time to digest. Again and again in the ensuing days there was the compulsive necessity to read the letter anew and wallow in the golden glow it projected over the future. This beguiled me down flowery paths into the siren land of 'If' where riches I had never known before would be mine if I found a home for one or two stories a month. Around me, in the poverty-stricken helplessness of those both in work and out of it, was material in abundance. Burning as I was with political bias for the establishment of social reform, I assured myself, ignorantly, that this fervid desire would be shared by editors in London. I wrote these tales and all came back with disappointing regularity. Now and then a kindly disposed editor would add a note to his rejection slip saying that, while he thought the story good of itself, its subject matter was not the sort of thing to interest his readers who paid their money for romance, entertainment and excitement. If I cared to send something of a lighter nature he would be happy to read it. Efforts I made in this direction foundered; my heart was not in them. The mirage of personal emancipation evaporated and, once again, the grim menace of the social scene which now wore its most villainous and unremitting aspect cast its shadow over the future.

Future? We had arrived at man's estate a decade ago. Time had conspired behind our backs to steal the years away. The moments of inward faltering had to be smothered and despondency taken by the scruff. The cure for these visitations was the therapy of a long walk usually, so as to avoid friends, through unfamiliar neighbourhoods all of which resembled each other and all furnished with their share of shabby men, young and old, at street corners, their like to be seen in ever-growing numbers throughout the land. Men for whom tomorrow would be a repetition of today and in whom hope's deceitful promise proclaimed its conquest in eyes that looked at you with dumb acceptance.

For two years a Labour Government had been in office. The rank and file of its supporters were now on the defence. ' ... and it's no use blaming Ramsay MacDonald. Look, man, the Liberals have only to vote with Stanley Baldwin and out goes Labour.' Monthly the Ministry published figures of the rising tide of new applicants signing on the dole. From one and a half to two millions, and now there were almost three; an army in the shadows, delivered from destitution only by the payment of a meagre unemployment benefit; a shabby dispirited host, pawns in a game whose machinery had seized up. Of what all this meant in terms of human degradation and misery the newspaper chroniclers were silent.

Their cry was 'Crisis' as gold began to flow from the country. To arrest this, the prescription was 'drastic economy' which, in the event, meant that those who had least were to get less. To staunch the haemorrhage of gold the financial pundits, who were like Mrs Boarder raising the wind at the pawnshop, sought an urgent transfusion in the shape of a loan from J. P. Morgan's bank in the United States. Morgan decided to oblige—on terms. These were that, since, in their view, the British Government's economies were not sufficiently drastic, it must pull in the nation's belt still further by a ten per cent cut in unemployment pay.

From the rebels of Clydeside, the Welsh valleys, the industrial North-west, Tyneside and London's East End came a roar of protest. The Labour Cabinet split on the issue. A minority declined to accept the bankers' terms and Ramsay MacDonald, having, it was said, listened to regal persuasion, decided to throw in his lot with Stanley Baldwin as head of a National Government.

The incongruity of Ramsay MacDonald paired in harness with Stanley Baldwin left thought stuttering. What was worse, the Labour leader was agreeable to the proposal of reducing the pittances paid to the millions who were out of work. On this the country had yet to have its say.

In the stormy General Election that ensued Ramsay MacDonald's National Government asked for a 'Doctor's Mandate'. A rumour flew round directed at the nervous and credulous which warned depositors in the Post Office Savings Bank that their money might be used for purposes not defined were a Labour Government to be elected.

The result was overwhelming. We, who were in the

Labour Club when the final result was declared, were silenced:

National Government   556<br>
Labour                 46

James Moleyns looked at our Divisional Agent, made a wry face, shrugged and said, 'Money wins again.'

# 38
# *Bankers' Benefit*

---

Suspended from wires above the long counter were placards on which, in large capitals and in sequence, the alphabet was printed: 'A–D', 'E–H', 'I–K' and so on. Each section had its queue of men, mostly shabby. Some of the elderly men, when boys, might have served a term of imprisonment for minor transgressions in what had been the derelict Reformatory School. This upper room had been the dormitory. Dismal and bare, adapted hurriedly to its present use years ago, its dirty windows looked on to a concrete exercise yard or playground encompassed by a high, unclimbable wall. Beyond rose the unlovely mass of the stinking gasworks. The room's filthy floor was uneven where the floorboards' softer parts had been scuffed away by boots and clogs, leaving the knotty parts and nailheads raised and polished. The wall decorations were either poster invitations to emigrate, to join the armed services, or warnings of sentences imposed on those who had drawn benefits by false representation.

Normally, at their bi-weekly attendances, the lines of dejected unemployed shuffled forward as each apathetic man 'signed on' or drew his dole, turned and trudged away in preoccupied silence counting the coins in his palm and reflecting dully on the life-limiting tale they told.

Today all apathy was gone. The street outside the playground's high wall, the playground itself and the long room where the men drew their dole were crowded, the voices of the men loud, harsh and angry, a volume of sound that intensified and increased as later comers, having their money pushed to them with ten per cent deducted, glared at the cashiers and denounced them angrily. Wearily the men on the counter's other side repudiated responsibility. 'No use blaming us. We're only carrying out orders.'

'Are you, be Christ. And have they docked your pay?'

'Next, please. You're holding up the job.'

'Job? What's that? I haven't seen soddin' work for over a year. And look at this,' a palm thrust out, money in it. 'How's she goina manage on this?'

As here, so it was at all places where men signed on. For the sake of convenience and to spread the load, applicants were given fixed times of attendance throughout the day. The news spread its wild-fire tale among all whose times of attendance were later. Apprehensive and incredulous, they came singly and in small groups to swell the crowd's turbulent and resentful indignation.

There were others, politically aware, to whom the blow had not come as any surprise. They were out now, haranguing the growing crowd, urging a march of protest to the Town Hall. They had brought banners tacked to poles: 'National Unemployed Workers' Movement', 'Work or Full Maintenance', and single placards nailed to laths whose lettering was the slap-dash work of amateurs. Still they came and, with the increase, a handful of police arrived under a superintendent and a serjeant's supervision. They were stationed singly and apart round the crowd's verge. The angry men now were roaring responses to the orators' denunciations. Finally, a motion of protest to be presented to the Town Council in the presence of all concerned was put to the meeting and carried with a great shout of 'Aye'.

Under the direction of a few organizers the crowd's formlessness was urged into ranks in the middle of the road-way, a long and multiplying crocodile, four deep, whose extremity soon passed round the corner. A large red flag was unfurled at the procession's head. A big drum material-ized from nowhere, it seemed, and, to its hollow and rhythmic beat, the march began towards the main road and the Town Hall. It was preceded by the Superintendent, the serjeant and a couple of constables, the rest of the police taking separate station either side the lines of marching men.

Before the main road was reached the Superintendent and his men about faced, the Super pointing with his stick to a side street running parallel with the main road and giving on to a secondary street which led, in a roundabout way, to a junction with the highway a couple of hundred yards or so from the square fronting the Town Hall.

There was a parley. The Superintendent was obdurate. The main road was forbidden. Angry shouts and catcalls. Men breaking line and being urged by the more disciplined to re-form ranks. The organizers submitted, the march resumed. People came to their front doors, eyes big with questioning, the menfolk being urged by the marchers to fall in and join the protest. Press photographers taking pictures. Other groups curious as to how the march would end followed as spectators. And now reinforcements, those on whom the burden of the cut would ultimately fall, indignant wives and mothers. They came clogged and shawled out of the side streets, angry, eyes aflame, and clattered along the crowded pavements, spilling into the roadway and, at points, merging with the men.

The Town Hall square was reached, the Manchester approach side blocked. Shopkeepers came to their doorways; the upper windows of offices were full of faces. By now the head of the procession had turned into the square and filled it from end to end, spreading like a river in spate across the main thoroughfare, jamming all traffic. High-ranking uniformed police stood in line on the broad, shallow steps fronting the Town Hall's entrance. Office staff looked on to the spectacle from the Hall's upper windows and a few elected representatives of the people came through the Hall's main doors to stand and stare in helplessness until they were required to withdraw by the police.

Catcalls, shouts, a babel of angry voices accompanied by the clangour of tramcar bells whose drivers hoped by this to persuade the jammed mass to make way. A signal from the Chief Superintendent provoked an instant and tumultuous roar of protest as, in answer to the signal, a troop of mounted police, followed by reinforcements on foot, came from their concealed stations of readiness to face the crowd in front of the steps. Another command and the police advanced. Placards being raised and lowered as the opposing forces pushed and pressed, the voice of the crowd took on a harsher, snarling tone. Helmets began to roll, truncheons were drawn and used; wrestlings, punchings, women reaching out to scratch and claw; placards being snatched and smashed, men going down, then, above the uproar, an unexpected reinforcement, the shrill alarm of fire-engine bells. Firemen appearing, running out hoses; the brassy glint of polished nozzles, then white, spitting shafts of water stabbing into the front and flanks of the struggling mass.

People cowering, tottering, stumbling, the drenched mass breaking into retreat. It was as though the Highways Cleansing Department had been set to work swilling down a rubbish-strewn square. The 'mob' dispersed, became individuals with names, Mrs Boarder, Michael McBride, James Moleyns, Jack Lashwood and others, all of fixed abode. With the exception of those who were taken to the cells or by ambulance to hospital they retreated in groups, defeated and sodden, making their sullen and embittered way home.

# 39

# Polly Put The Kettle On

Segregation asserted itself in subtle ways. Those who were out of work tended to avoid their luckier counterparts and the embarrassment was mutual. Pay day brought a constrained uneasiness. 'Where are we going tonight?' The customary question of a week-end among friends was avoided if, standing by in the group, were any whose pockets were known to be empty. For those who had a job, the sight of friends to whom all doors of entertainment and conviviality were closed could bring sharp, apprehensive shivers, aware as they were that this fate could be anybody's in these uncertain times. Sometimes compassionate sisters, brothers and parents, when nobody else was in the house, slipped a sixpence: 'There you are, lad. It's all I can spare.'

For me there was the sustaining and unquenchable hope of another windfall, despite the discouraging and persistent rejection of the stories I was sending the rounds. Instead of the puffed-up and fatuous dream of selling two a month I was reduced to the threadbare hope of placing two a year, and even in this I had to admit that, for all I knew, the land of 'If' might again be trailing its fanciful promise, luring and beckoning only to deceive. But what had reality to offer by way of alternative? The prison of an office job, if one could be landed, at twenty shillings a week? No, let the newspapers shout 'Workshy', and 'Letters to the Editor' throw the jibe 'Weary Willies' at the unemployed, where I was concerned, and while the diminished dole was there to help pay my corner at home I was determined to pursue the star and take whatever came by way of consequences, be these what they may.

Secretly, as a spur to effort, I played a game with nature.

My usual route on my daily walk to Manchester took me along Broad Street, Windsor Bridge, the Crescent and Chapel Street, one of whose bow-fronted shops was reputed to be the original around which Harold Brighouse had written his famous play *Hobson's Choice*.

The Crescent is what its name implies. It is an embankment looking down on to the murky River Irwell which here, describing a loop, cascades over a weir to drag its poisoned length through Broughton and on to mark the boundary of Manchester and Salford. For years its farther bank had been a municipal tip and, later, a recreation ground. The nearer steep embankment nurtures a number of stunted, smoke-blackened thorn trees, and it was with these my game was played. A winter game when shrivelling winds from the north and east had swept the branches bare and killed another year. Another barren year — and there was the sting. Perhaps, between now and springtime when all the world was new once more, effort would be rewarded. Perhaps. November's acrid fogs, the ice and snows of the New Year giving way to the hoops and whips and tops of emergent kids in February and their marble games in the wild winds of March; these were the furlong posts of my race with time. Before the black twigs of the thorn took on the faintest haze of green, would Fortune relax and smile once again? The answer was the question mark.

There was the other threat impending on all for whom there was no work, the inquisition of the Means Test. All who applied for transitional benefit after they had reached the permissive limit had to present themselves before the Public Assistance Committee for questioning according to the requirements of Form 7. Those who had been called to judgment came to the Labour Club for help and advice.

Mickmac, mesmerized with bewilderment and quite unable to grasp the fact that he had been denied the weekly pittance, confronted the Divisional Agent. 'But I'm out o' work. I told 'em: "Find me a job," I said. "Find me a job. Anythin'. Aye, anythin'. I don't care what it is, I'll do it." '

'It's the economy drive, Mick. You're not the only one.' He waved his hand towards me: 'It'll be the same for him when his benefit's run out. His mother and sister're working. The Public Assistance Committee will rule that his family has to maintain him. And there's no appeal.'

'But what am I goina do?' Mickmac murmured, staring.

'If you went to live in digs as a single man they'd have to give you transitional relief.'

We went out.

'Wharram I goina say to me mam?' Mickmac mumbled, as we walked. He glanced at me. 'I thought he'd have done summat. I voted Labour, you know.'

I reminded him, without enthusiasm, of his only alternative, and, while I spoke, there came the chill admission that when my benefit ran out I, then, would be in his shoes. He answered me on a note of puzzled irritability, 'You could say it's the same thing as me livin' at home, can't you? What's the difference between me goin' in digs and livin' at home? What *is* the difference? Go on, tell us, then.' When I held my tongue he mumbled, 'An' who's gonna take me in, anyway, wi' nowt in my pocket?'

'There's Polly,' I suggested. 'She took Alfie in, didn't she? And you would get transitional benefit ... '

Through her open door we saw her removing her hat-pins while she stood at the table chatting to Mrs Boarder who was pacing to and fro nursing Hetty's squalling child. ' ... been to put some flowers on my mother's grave. It's her birthday. And after I'd come out of Edgecroft cemetery I thought "Right, Polly Mytton, it's years since you went round the old haunts." ' She interrupted herself. 'Let's see, now, when *was* it I gave up my dandelion and burdock business? Ay, years and years ago. Anyway, Annie, I thought I'd take a look round the fields where I used to gather the herbs ... '

8

Mrs Boarder interrupted, incredulously. 'You mean you've *walked* all that way, Polly?'

'Oh, aye. It's this.' She gave her right hip a slap. 'Been giving me a bit o' trouble lately, so I thought, "Right, and there's only one thing for that. Walk it off." '

'There's nowt much wrong with your hip if you walked all that way. Why, woman, it's five miles or more.' She sat, rocking the child to and fro.

Polly let the comment pass, removed her coat and said: 'Anyway, Annie, I tell you, when I got there—fields, did you say? You should see it now, swarmin' with property. Making fortune upon fortune that Nobby Clarke is.' She sighed, heavily. 'Made me feel real down in the dumps, lass,' a headshake, 'Lordy me, how times do change.' She saw us at the door. 'And what do you two rapscallions want?'

Embarrassed, Mickmac haltingly told his tale.

Mrs Boarder slapped the table, threw her glance ceiling-wards, shook her head and cried, angrily, 'The buggerin' limit, this is. My Christ, Jim Moleyns is right, the rich, rotten bastards win again.' She glared at Polly who had her fingers to her lips. 'Driven from home, eh? That's it now, is it?' She shook her head again. 'May God forgive 'em.'

Mickmac continued, ' ... and the feller at the Labour Club he said if I can find digs to live in they'll have to gie me the money. So, I thought, like ... if I could sleep here, like ... ' He added, hastily, 'I'd want nowt off you to eat.'

'Bless you, lad,' said Polly. 'O' course you can stay an' welcome. Here,' she added, walking to the fireplace where she set the kettle on the cross-bars: 'I don't know about you lot but I'm just in the mood for a nice cup o' tea.'

# 40

# *Beyond the Pale*

After he had told me that my unemployment benefit was exhausted the clerk added, in the weary tone of one who had used the phrase far too often: 'Sign on Tuesday and Friday for your health insurance stamp.'

There was no appeal. Last week I had been on the unemployed army's pay roll; from now on I would be a ranker in the other army which had no public claim on the bounty of this earth. The blank notice-board 'Situations Vacant' flaunted its spiteful joke, as did the coloured recruiting posters plastered at intervals along the walls. I walked out of the office. I could, of course, put in an application to the Public Assistance Committee.

'Have you any stocks and shares, bank deposits or investments of any kind? Any unnecessary item of furniture? How much does your mother earn? What are your sister's wages?' You knew in advance what the verdict would be. It went without saying that there would be sympathetic understanding at home and any suggestion of moving into digs indignantly rejected, but this, consoling as it was, did not take the edge off the sense of humiliating frustration nor the bitter knowledge that, but for the good fortune of free board and lodgings at home, I was but this step removed from beggary. No man was invulnerable. A university degree did not afford protection. At the docks, Chief Engineers and Extra Chiefs waited, ready and willing to take on any work below their rank. Welsh choirs from the valleys were parading the gutters of main streets of towns far from home singing for coppers and, to call London's attention to conditions beyond the metropolis, plans were being laid for hunger marches organized to converge simultaneously on the capital. It made a man feel daft, superfluous and banished to a no-man's-land beyond the pale of human fellowship. This was it, then, the end product of the deliberations of high finance. No, no, not quite the end, for I had a home. Even Mickmac, lodging with Polly Mytton, had not yet struck bottom. That was reached when you were adrift 'on the road', seeking lodgings for the night in casual wards. I wasn't likely to reach that, but it was there. Ought I to look for lodgings? I knew how this proposal would be received at home where my doleful or, rather, dole-less tale had yet to be told.

By the time I returned from a purposely protracted walk my mother and sister were home from work. My sister looked up from the library novel she was reading. 'You'll like this,' she said. 'Upton Sinclair's *Oil*, and', she went on, warningly, '*I'm* reading it first. I've had my name down for it for weeks.'

Mother took an envelope from the mantel. 'James Moleyns left this. It's for you to type for the Labour paper. And he said he wants you to call at London Road Station tomorrow. It's a Rambling Club he's forming for the Labour League of Youth. Every Sunday walking all over Derbyshire. Now what *was* it he wanted?' She scratched behind her ear. 'Oh, dear. What a memory.'

My sister exclaimed impatiently at Mother's forgetfulness. 'He wants you to find out how many tickets have to be bought to get the reduced fare.'

'There is no need to snap, young lady,' Mother rebuked. 'I was only gathering my thoughts.' She looked at me. 'James Moleyns said he called twice this afternoon and you weren't in. What have you been doing with yourself?'

'Wasting his substance in riotous living,' my sister said, facetiously. This was ignored.

I made my confession and, to my surprise, it was taken philosophically. 'Oh, well,' Mother said, on a sigh that

stung me, 'we knew it was coming. Ah, well, keep your
pecker up, lad. We've come through worse times than this
and here we are, still alive to tell the tale.'

'And what a blooming tale it is,' my sister said warmly as
she looked at me. 'From the sound of it, Mother will be
signing on next year.'

'It's the Executive Committee,' Mother explained.
'They've decided that when any of the staff reach sixty we've
to go. But,' she added, 'they said they'd give me a good
reference.'

My sister laughed scoffingly. 'She's worked for them since
1915 and they say they'll give her a good reference. Impu-
dence! I should jolly well think they would. That's religion
for you.'

'We'll manage, like we've always done, never fear. We
never know what's in store and ... '

'Oh, Mother,' my sister protested, 'this looking on the
bright side gets on my nerves. What this country wants is a
blessed revolution.'

'I am *quite* aware of that, young lady,' Mother answered,
straightening her back. 'And let me remind you that your
grandfather and I were out with the Independent Labour
Party long before you were born.' She glanced at me and
pointed dramatically to the typewriter. 'As for you, your job
is there and don't you ever forget it. You've proved you can
do it. What's been done once can be done again.'

It was consoling to be the recipient of such confidence even
though my prospects were no more than a promissory note
whose security, for immediate practical purpose, could be
equated with that of the German million-mark notes that
were being peddled for pennies as jokes by gutter traders.
No matter which way I looked at it, the present revealed me
to be what I was, an involuntary sponger on the family
exchequer, a unit of a vast and growing army which had its
counterpart in every nation of the Continent, not to mention

the unnumbered who shuffled daily along the breadlines of the United States of America.

The next day, coming out of the Inquiry Office at Manchester's London Road Station, I saw Mickmac standing between a couple of suitcases a pace distant from a plump lady who was at the ticket office. He saw me, winked and silently mouthed, 'I'll not be a minute,' then, a suitcase in either hand, he followed his patroness to the train, leaving me to stroll after him to wait at the barrier. As he returned I saw him engaged in altercation with a railway porter.

'Their flamin' cheek,' he complained to me, indignantly. 'We're standin' in all weathers at the tram stop, hump the bags all the way up the approach and those lousy sods say we should hand over inside the station. Well, you know what they can do, don't you? Aye, and they're on wages and a uniform. They forget all about that.' We walked down the slope of the approach, pausing on the pavement by the tram stop where a number of shabby youths and men were lined against the wall. Mickmac took his place at the line's farther end.

'Any luck?' the scarecrow youth next in line asked.

'Thrippence,' Mickmac answered, then, in peeved tones, reported his brush with the porter, concluding, 'They get their share from the taxis don't they?'

A tramcar stopped. One of the alighting passengers stood to one side until all were down, then asked the guard to hand his luggage from under the stairs.

'There y'are. There y'are,' Mickmac's colleagues called eagerly to the man at the head of the queue. He ran to the tram and touched his cap saying, ingratiatingly: 'Carry your bag, sir? Carry your bag?'

Mickmac was saying: 'They say you can do all right at Christmas-time and holidays. Not so good just now, though.' He sighed. 'I tried at Jackson's Emporium. Door-to-door canvassin' on commission.' A shrug. 'Turned me down. I can't help me clothes, can I? Oh, well, this is better than nowt.'

I wasn't paying much attention to what he was saying. My eyes were on the obsequious unofficial porter abasing himself hopefully. With a jolt, the spectacle took thought back a quarter of a century when, pinafored, I was, once again, with Mickmac and the barefoot children outside the mills and factories at the end of the day's work. 'Carry your bag, sir? Carry your bag?' merged into ghostly echoes of childish supplication: 'Any bread, cake or pie? Any bread, cake or pie?'

# 41

# You Never Know Your Luck

Once upon a time Jackson's Emporium in the seedy swarming backwaters of a Manchester slum had been a miscellany of small shops. These had been converted into miniature departmental stores catering for those who habitually relied on the system of weekly repayments for the provision of their requirements in clothing, footwear and general household things.

Chadman, the manager, a small prowling lath of a man, lorded it over the staff of girl assistants. He took long strides, walking with the bouncing gait often affected by those who are undersized. He was zealous, his eyes everywhere and, when speaking to the collector salesmen, he had a habit of baring his teeth and thumping his left palm with his clenched fist by way of urging the necessity for greater effort on their part. He wore a double-breasted, tight-fitting blue suit, a blue and white polka-dotted bow tie and brown shoes, highly polished, which he protected with black galoshes when walking home in the rain. He was overawed by his employer, who seemed to find the show of grovelling obsequiousness not at all embarrassing or displeasing. The elderly proprietor was a paunchy, shuffling man, a church-warden and the possessor of a big and flashy car from which Chadman and the girl assistants were perpetually chasing the local kids. His office, marked 'Private', was upstairs at the rear of the premises and overlooked the backyards and chimney-pots of the crumbling houses opposite. Here, when not poring over correspondence, figures, percentages and samples, he received commercial travellers dealing in sweat-shop merchandise whom he badgered and bullied over pennies and discounts.

Chadman, folding his arms and slowly rubbing his lower lip with a rigid forefinger, looked me up and down appraisingly, then went into a detailed interrogation as to my previous experience.

'Right,' he said, finally. 'We'll give you a trial. The pay's a pound a week basic. There's half a crown paid for every new customer you get—incentive, see? And we pay ten per cent commission on all you collect over ten pounds a week. The more we pay you the better we like it. No limit. Build up your collections to two hundred pounds a week and there you are—twenty quid a week wages. Oh, and when you're canvassing, here's a tip: when you get a new customer check up on their rent and insurance books—see they're not in arrears. *Reg*'lar payers, that's what we want.'

I asked him to define the territory I would be expected to work. He regarded me as one puzzled, then, with a suppressed sardonic laugh, added: 'It's up to our men to get in where they can. Anywhere. Territory, eh? We're in business. It's catch as catch can. Right? Okay.' He pointed to a half-glazed door marked 'General Office'.

'Secretary in there. Give her your cards.'

The secretary-bookkeeper was a blonde young lady with pale-blue eyes which regarded you with languor. She was thin, flat-chested and given to wearing blouses with frilly cuffs and collars. She instructed me in the mysteries of filling up the simplest of application forms and, without looking at me, concluded: 'Repayments are at the rate of a shilling in the pound. The first shilling of each pound goes as poundage charges.'

I heard the door being opened. She looked past me, brightness coming into her eyes as she smiled animatedly. She turned, pushed an electric kettle's plug into its socket and picked up a teapot. The breezy man who stood aside as I went out wore his bowler hat at a jaunty angle; blue-eyed and blond, his close-trimmed moustache and general bearing gave him a military air. He had draped his folded raincoat over his left arm and, conspicuously, he held an account book stuffed with application forms. Bicycle clips jingled on his wrist. He oozed self-confidence and self-esteem and, as I was soon to learn, went by the nickname of Colonel Bogey among the envious other salesmen-collectors. I closed the office door to the tinkle of teacups and, going out of the shop, all but collided with a morose individual who had just balanced his bicycle against the kerb. He wore a velour felt hat whose brim, fashionably, was pulled down all round, a soiled raincoat and thick-soled boots. Steel spectacles hung midway on his beak-like nose and his lugubrious eyes looked at me over the top of these. 'Oh,' he said, regarding my issue of application forms. 'Just started, eh?'

'Yes.'

He shook his head and sighed. 'He knows what he's doin'.'

'Who?'

'Fat Boy, the churchwarden, the boss. You know the drill with him, don't you? Him and Short Arse in there. Hold all the cards, that pair. "Catch as catch can" eh? My Christ, isn't it, now?' He shook his head and launched into a discouraging jeremiad. 'Twenty quid a week, he trotted that one out, I suppose? Look at me, then. Typical. Manchester—Ancoats, Moss Side, Hulme; then into Salford, Docks Ward, St Thomas's Ward, St Mathias's and St Luke's, all over Regent Road and Debtors' Retreat. Twelve hours and more a day I put in. Three new customers outa two weeks' canvassin', then Short Arse turns two of 'em down. "Bad risk," he says.' He indicated the new bike parked at the kerb. 'Colonel Bogey's in, I see. Well, bollocks to him for a starter. Cock happy, that's him.' He raised his brows: 'I'll tell you summat else. He'll get copped. One of his customers' husbands'll walk in one day while he's on the job or my name's not Sam Grogan. And serve the bastard right. 'T'isn't fair. Eh? You need to ask. What happens if any of us gets the bullet? Here we all are, working like blacks in all weathers—door to friggin' door building up a book—and who gets all your customers if Short Arse or Fat Boy gives you the chopper? Colonel Bogey, star salesman, he gets the lot. The Titless Wonder, her up in the office, she sees to that.' He moved to the shop door. 'Good luck, mate. You'll be needin' it.'

For me there wasn't anything novel in this business of knocking on people's front doors. Elections, parliamentary and municipal, had given me and others plenty of experience canvassing the Labour interest. But to exercise this for the benefit of Messrs Jackson's Emporium and myself induced, at first, a self-conscious tongue-tied diffidence until I remembered the pound a week basic which would take care of my corner at home.

For the initiation I chose a district well away from our neighbourhood.

'Good morning, madam. I am representing Jackson's Emporium. Can I interest you in ... '

'No thank you.'

'Not today.'

'He doesn't believe in weekly payments.'

'You'll have to come when she's home from work.'

'Clothes? It's grub we want and the bloody rent.'

'No, you *can't*. Fed up, I am, answering the door every half hour.'

After several hours of this fruitless endeavour Chadman's 'Build up your collections to two hundred pounds a week and there you are,' became a mockery. Suppose, by week-end, I hadn't landed a solitary customer? I saw myself attending the office on pay day with my tale of diligence unrewarded but I could not see Chadman or the secretary parting with a pound.

'Good morning, madam. I am representing ... '

Sam Grogan's words came to mind: 'Ten hours a day I've put in. Three customers out o' two weeks' canvassing … ' This was what he meant. It was evening now; people were returning from work. I could, of course, do some fishing in home waters. There were Polly Mytton, Annie Boarder and other neighbours, but diffidence reminded me that this smacked too much of begging. No, that could be exercised only as a last and desperate resort. Meanwhile, peg away here for another hour.

'Good evening, madam. I am calling on behalf of Jackson's Emporium.'

'Whose?' She was a woman of fifty or so whose hair was done in a tight bun. Her hands were powdered with flour. I explained. She rubbed her right nostril with her knuckle and then, having sniffed, lifted her apron and wiped the flour smear from her nose. 'Do you do evenin' dress?'

'Oh, yes,' I assured her promptly, hoping this to be the case.

'Made to measure, o' course,' she said warningly.

'Of course. You can go tonight to be measured. The shop's open until eight.'

'Oh, it's not for me,' she said. 'You'd better come in.' I followed. Two men were at the table eating their evening meal. A heap of half-kneaded dough lay on a cleared corner of the table. 'It's for our George, there.' Our George grinned at me. He was a plump young man in his early twenties and he had a shock of black, curly hair. She smiled at him then said to me, proudly: 'L.R.A.M. Just won it. Cap and gown, eh? Yes. Full-time job, music, for him now. Playing the piano at the new super-cinema.' She smiled again at her son who said, bashfully, 'Aw. Go on, Ma.'

She addressed me again. 'It's *full* evening dress he wants — and in an 'urry. The lot, mind, shirts, collars and all of it. What'll it cost?'

'Well — h'm — off-hand … I could let you know in a couple of minutes. Is there a telephone around here?'

'Post office,' George said. 'Round the corner.'

He was splashing about under the tap when I returned. His fond mother said, 'All right,' when I told her the cost. 'Oh, and I forgot,' she went on as I filled in the form, 'Patent leather pumps. Put a pair of them down. Hurry up, there, George.' After she had signed she confided, with a wink, 'Aye, and when he's fitted out he's going to be photographed, aye, *and* in his cap and gown, too. They might print it in the *Pendleton Reporter*.' Her husband, who during the whole of the transaction never once had spoken nor looked up from his newspaper, suddenly pushed his plate away, rose, belched loudly and, with newspaper in hand, went into the backyard.

I withdrew, congratulating myself on having broken the ice and earned half a crown. In our street I overtook Polly Mytton lugging a shopping bag filled with potatoes. 'Ay, thank you, lad,' she said when I relieved her of the burden. 'Been doing a bit of shopping for me and Annie Boarder. And you're looking pleased with yourself, I must say.'

I told her of my good luck.

'Well, now, isn't that a very funny thing?' she said as we went into her house.

'What's that, Polly?'

'Why, here I've been waiting for one of Jackson's men to come round again. Not that I'm a believer in weekly payments. For myself I'd rather go without until I can put the money down, that's how we were brought up in the old days. But there's Alfie—Listen to me! Ay, I wonder how that lad's going on?—I meant Mick McBride, o' course. He'll have to have a new pair o' boots. Poor lad's all but walkin' on the blackin'. So put me down for a shillin' a week, will you, and let's see him proper shod. Don't know where the money'll come from but never fear, the Lord will provide. He always has done up to now.' She had placed half a dozen potatoes on the table. She gave the rest of them in the bag to me.

'Pass 'em in to Annie Boarder as you go by, lad.' She shook
her head. 'Poor lass. I don't like the look of her. Don't like it
at all. Ay, deary me. What a life she's had.'

Suddenly Mickmac burst into the room, panting heavily,
his eyes alight.

'Whatever's the matter?' Polly demanded.

'Can't believe it, Polly. I just can't believe it. I've gorra
job. Reg'lar job. Father Borelli sent me. I've told me mam.
It's true. Weaste cemetery, grave-diggin'. Oh, heck!'

'Well, I never!' Polly said, flopping into her chair. 'God
bless my soul!'

# 42

# *Stocktaking*

---

The wood-cased and glazed war memorial on the street wall which had been paid for by a door-to-door collection seemed to sum up the situation. In 1919 we who were in our early teens had stood with ex-servicemen, young and ageing mothers and widows, in a semicircle at the service of dedication. Thirteen years now had passed. Summer suns had erased the rubricated initials of the soldiers' and sailors' names. The memorial's casing had warped and the howling winds of bygone winters had driven in the rains to smear and blotch the black lettering. Street ball games had cracked the glazing, then, when the screws holding the case to the wall rusted away, it collapsed. When it was no longer there nobody missed it.

Thirteen years since the war had come to an end. There was Bert Harrington's son who had never seen his father; there he was, his dad's spit and image, now finished his schooling and in his first year's apprenticeship at Marlowe's Engineering works. In five years' time, should there be another war, he would be of military age: in seven years' time, if there weren't a war and if things continued as at present, he would have served his time and been fired because he then would be qualified to draw the full rate of pay.

Seven years from now. It did not bear thinking on. It was 1932. In December I would be in my thirtieth year and as all in like case, skint and confronted with a future best described by the new Beatitude which was going the rounds: 'Blessed he is that expects nothing for he surely will not be disappointed.'

Yet I was lucky in not being one of the groups of scarecrow spectres at street corners or, if the weather were severe, on the shadowy benches of the billiard halls. Indeed I had two occupations, writing a novel and taking as little time off from this as was necessary to keep my weekly collections for Jackson's Emporium just above the ten pounds a week mark, the ten per cent commission being my face-saver at home. As for future prospects for all left out in the cold ... The three million registered as being on the dole did not include the debarred who were being supported by parents or married children. Trade union membership had shrunk to the level of 1913 and men and women who had dreamed dreams of Jerusalem in England's green and pleasant land saw, in the spectral ranks of the unemployed, the tarnished face of Empire.

For no reason at all Mrs Boarder came to mind. A few weeks ago she had been taken to hospital and the latest news Polly Mytton had brought from a visit was that Annie Boarder was fading away. 'Shadow of herself,' Polly said to my mother. ' "Don't prolong the agony." That's what she said when I tried to cheer her up.'

'Oh, dear,' Mother said on a heavy sigh. 'What a life that poor lass has had.'

What a life indeed. A hopeless, endless struggle that would end with a cheap funeral, a wreath from the neighbours and an unmarked grave.

'And what's singular about that?' James Moleyns commented when we were alone in our house discussing the dismal subject. 'Isn't that the way for most of us? It's daft to expect anything different with the cards stacked against you like they are right from the start. But don't set me off. I'm not in the mood.'

The discussion was interrupted by Polly Mytton. She pushed the door wide and, brows arched indignantly, entered without announcement. 'Do you know what they've done?' she declared, staring at me: 'They've sent her a summons. Jackson's. Sent her a summons. Postman's just brought it. Hetty's frightened to death.'

We went back with her. Hetty looked at me apprehensively as Polly, with a '*There* it is,' slapped her palm on the quarto sheet of blue paper folded into three to imitate a County Court summons; she then flopped into a chair and resumed pulling and stretching the clippings of chamois leather heaped in the table's centre. Hetty, with her ancient hand sewing-machine, was fashioning the leather off-cuts into small window-cleaning squares. She looked hopefully from me to James. 'Do you know anybody who could go for me? I mean—you see—well, it's the time I'd lose.'

The paper had been designed to deceive the simple into thinking it an official document, a rigmarole of pseudo-legal terminology, threatening, unless payment of arrears were made 'within seven days', the issue of a COUNTY COURT SUMMONS. These frightening words were set in heavy Gothic type. 'Don't take any notice of it, Hetty,' I assured her. 'Look.' I crumpled the paper into a ball and tossed it into the fire. 'They don't take people to court for the few shillings you owe.'

'I know who I'd like to take to court,' Polly said with unusual fervour. She pointed to the little pile of finished window leathers above the sewing-machine. 'Penny each, that's all he's paying her. Dawn till dark she's at it to make a livin'. And there they are in The Bazaar. Sixpence a time, that's what they're chargin'.'

Hetty was looking at me, I at her. Her red-rimmed eyes and her dull expression of utter weariness were both poignant and infuriating. 'No kiddin'? I haven't to go to court?' she asked. I assured her again. 'Oh,' she said on a relieved sigh. 'I keep expecting he'll write from America. Don't even know where he is. Ay, money, money, money, but, thank God, I've not got behind with the rent.'

James Moleyns had stood there with his lips compressed. 'Hetty. Listen,' he said, suddenly, then rested his palms on the table and leaned towards her. 'Listen to me, Hetty. You've got to do as I've told you before and no more nonsense.'

'I'm not going to the Guardians,' she answered, emphatically.

'Why won't you believe me? I've told you: they were done away with three years ago. It's true, I tell you, true. The workhouse is being pulled down. It's gone and all that went with it.'

'Hark to what he says, love,' Polly said, then glanced at James. 'Who does she go to see then, Jim?'

'I'll tell you who, Polly. She comes with me tonight to see Dr Macaulay.' He held up his hand as Hetty was about to speak: 'If you won't believe me then listen to him. He's on the Council now. Let him do the telling. There's no disgrace in it. It's not workhouse charity any more. You'll get an allowance to help with the rent. And there's your baby to think of. You'll get something for him. The way you're going on, woman, you'll be laid up.'

'But it's ... '

'It's your rights. What the dickens do you think we've been fighting for all these years? Get that charity business out of your mind.' He concluded, flatly, 'But I'm not listening to anything you say. You're coming with me and that's that.' He took up a handful of chamois cuttings and flung them down again. 'As for this ... In 1932? My God!'

# 43

# 'Marvellous, Isn't It?'

'What a life she's had.' To me the recollection of my mother's comment was Mrs Boarder's epitaph. Looking from our doorstep I watched the hearse pull away. When it and its following solitary car turned the corner the crowd of neighbours, which included Mrs Moleyns, her father, like a silver-haired biblical patriarch, Polly Mytton with Hetty's child on her arm, slowly dispersed. I wound up our paper blind which, like everybody else's, had been drawn as the usual mark of respect.

What a life, indeed. Except for a one day's excursion by waggonette into the Cheshire countryside I never knew Annie Boarder to have had a holiday in the accepted sense. As with many of us it had been a case of mother and children walking to the public park with a food-stuffed basket, a penn'orth of boiling water from the café to make a jug of tea, and a picnic on the grass listening to the band. Well, she now had joined the company of the anonymous host in the oblivion of a nameless grave — and that was that.

Four o'clock, Friday afternoon. Pay day. In two hours I would be on the knocker collecting the weekly repayments for Jackson's Emporium. In some instances it was a case of if Peter were paid, then Paul had to whistle and had to be first among the rival collectors next week.

Two hours to go. My eye was caught by the Opera House programme lying atop yesterday's *Manchester Guardian*, both of which Mother had brought home late last night.

> British National Opera Company.
> Le Coq d'Or (Rimsky-Korsakov)
> Conductor: Sir Thomas Beecham

I recalled her expression. It was the same each time she returned from the opera or a concert, that of one transported. 'Oh! What an evening. "Hymn to the Sun"! "The Golden Cockerel", Beecham conducting,' taking off her hat then holding up her right hand as though swearing upon oath. 'If ever I come into a fortune I'd give it to Tommy Beecham for all the pleasure I've had.'

'There. You see,' my sister said, looking up from her eternal dressmaking and throwing me a glance. 'We're disinherited before she's got it.'

'Oh,' Mother retorted, loftily and with a backhand wave, 'you'd have your share, young lady. Never fear.' She passed me the programme and the *Guardian*. 'Put it with the others when you've looked at it. And I see James Moleyns has been in the wars. We came home together on the tram. How did he get that black eye?'

'Fascist meeting in the Free Trade Hall. The strong-arm Blackshirt boys chucked us out.'

Mother shook her head. 'Fighting in the Free Trade Hall! Whatever is the world coming to?'

I opened the *Guardian* to read what its critic had to say of the opera. My eye was caught by a middle-page photograph. It was of an elderly German Jew with an insulting placard hanging from his neck. He sat, cross-legged, dignified and resigned, in the middle of a hand-cart and was being publicly paraded by jeering, jack-booted Nazis.

A brisk rap on the door. James Moleyns grinning and bubbling with excitement. 'I can't believe it,' he announced, planting himself on the hearth-rug. 'The impossible's happened. I've got a job! No kidding. I start Monday.' He stretched his arms and laughed. 'Wages again! Two pounds five a week! Forty-five bob! Me! She's already planning a spending spree, the missis.' He blew his lips out and shook his head. 'It's like a dream.' He became serious. 'There's thorns with the rose as per usual, of course. You know what's starting the wheels turning? Musso and Hitler. And who's put up the money for their capers? Neither of 'em had any to start with. Look at 'em now. Both got armies. Somebody's forked out in a big way.'

'You're going on armaments?'

'Marvellous, isn't it?' A head-shake. 'Money can always be found for that—and we haven't paid for the last scrap yet. My gad, it makes you cynical, but if you let yourself dwell on it you'd end up in Prestwich Lunatic Asylum.'

'Don't dwell on it, then.'

He shrugged and picked up the theatre programme. 'I came home with your mother last night. She was full of the opera.' He waved the programme and grinned. 'Another for the collection. Lord, look at them all!' We looked at the tight-packed double row on the top shelf of the bookcase. 'Well,' he said, 'whatever else she might have missed she didn't miss that.'

I remembered that she was within sight of being turned off at work because of age. Each time that this came to mind it stuck in the gizzard even though I knew that to be discarded thus was the common lot. It rankled and I said so. 'I know,' James answered. 'Makes you want to let fly. But that's no good. Look—' He pointed to Grandfather's collection of Socialist literature: 'There he was, before we were born, getting on with it. Never you fear, lad, the moneybags won't get away with it for ever.'

He was at the table now looking at the paper in the typewriter. 'Mmmm!' he murmured. 'Page 259, eh? We're getting on. How's it coming?'

'Let me get to the end, then I'll tell you.'

He walked to the door where he turned, smiled and winked. 'Keep at it, lad. You never know your luck. Be seeing you.'

# 44

# *Turn of the Tide*

Those are the happy moments in a writer's life when a tale takes complete possession. For months this one had held me in thrall. Theme, characters and development flowed to within sight of completion, then, that curse of curses, a dead end and the frustrating and jeering challenge of an empty page. I was in process of learning that I was involved not with rules and applications of logic but with the unpredictable, the incalculable, and that this could vanish, abruptly, without notice. All I could do was to look into the empty well yearning for the waters to flow again.

Such had been my overweening confidence that, passing the river bank on the Crescent and having seen the winds of late autumn strip the blackened thorn tree of its last leaf, I had told the bush that its budding next spring would not, once again, mark another year of fruitless effort. I had, indeed, gone further. I had assured it that by mid-November the book would be in a publisher's hands and that just before Christmas he would have accepted it. What a Christmas present! What a Christmas! What ho! And what a fool who prematurely counts his chickens.

Morose, cantankerous, anti-social and quite ignoring the interests of Jackson's Emporium I sought a solution in long, aimless and solitary walks. Finally, as though gravitating naturally to the appropriate place, I wandered round the vast acreage of the cemetery to read epitaphs of those who had died rich enough to be able to afford a gravestone. White marble angels tootling on marble trumpets or holding up arms supplicatingly as they stared lugubriously at the dirty skies: marble crosses and marble anchors all darkened with films of grime. Standing stones, once perpendicular, but many, from neglect now inclining at various drunken angles. Beyond these, desolation: the mounds of the nameless multitude all covered with dead weeds and shrivelled grasses nodding in the wintry wind.

Incongruously there floated to my ears the half-muffled masculine warblings of someone not at all displeased with life:

'The bells are ringing for me and my girl.
The parson's waiting, for me and my girl.'

Clods of earth were being thrown out of a grave some yards away. The vocalist's coat was folded and lying on a sack next a heap of salvaged wreath frames.

Mickmac. Since he had started work I had seen little or nothing of him. He beamed at me, scrambled out of the grave and offered me a cigarette. 'By gum,' he said, 'this job is ... ' he held up his thumb and winked. 'I love it. An' you're not rushed so long as you're on time with the job. See this lot?' He touched the wreath frames with his toe. 'Superintendent lets me have as many as I've a mind. Tanner a time they fetch at the florist's shop. You've got to be smart: the kids've cottoned on. Chuck 'em over the wall to their mates. Aye, *and* on the day of the funeral sometimes.' He took a long draw of his cigarette, gave a little cough, then glanced at me. 'You've heard, I suppose?'

'What about?'

He grinned. 'I'm gettin' wed. Well, I can afford it now, can't I? Regular job. Er—' He rubbed his nose then pulled his ear, continuing, awkwardly, 'I'd've given you the order for Jackson's but—I mean—you see—well, it's her mother. She's a member of the Co-op. Made me get a clothin' coupon from the Co-op for my weddin' suit an' things, then she gets the divi. I was goin' to give you the order. Really.'

I told him not to worry about it.

'Well, I do. I don't forget. Aye, and there's Polly Mytton.

I'd do anything for her and if I come up in the Irish Sweep I'll see that she's all right. Comes here every week she does with a little bunch o' flowers for her ma's and pa's grave. O'er there, it is. Goin' to be buried with 'em, she says. Oh, aye, and she brings a few for Annie Boarder. Cripes! Couldn't believe it when we put Annie down. Big woman like that. Light as a feather.' He nipped off the glow from his cigarette and put the fag end behind his ear. 'Better be getting on with it. Be seeing you.'

'Getting on with it.' O, dullard brain. O, passing, barren days, is the well to be dry for ever? If only writing were a science based on facts and principles wherein you were certain that all problems were ultimately susceptible of rational solution! The land of 'If' again.

At home, maternal concern. 'Whatever is the matter with you these days, going around like a bear with a sore head?'

Sisterly facetiousness that infuriated. 'It's love. It must be. "O Romeo, Romeo! wherefore art thou Romeo?" '

'Now where are you off to?'

Night walks in the quiet of suburbia to invoke sky, moon and stars. Then, one late afternoon on the third circuit of the public park's perimeter, revelation, and the vexing problem was gloriously resolved and captured in scribbled synopsis.

My confidence was such that a little over a month before Christmas I posted copies simultaneously to two eminent publishers, hoping that, before December 24th, they would be duelling fiercely with cheque books as weapons. A few days before Christmas the postman handed me, together with some Christmas cards, a package with one of the publisher's labels prominently displayed. Deflated, confounded, I opened the package.

Dear Sir,
    We have read your novel with great interest. Unfortunately our Spring List is to include a book on a similar

theme translated from the German, Mr Hans Fallada's 'Little Man, What Now' ...

Oh, well. Never say die. There was the other publisher who, doubt whispered spitefully, might also at this moment be sending the book back.

Christmas gone. The New Year. It was one of those bitter January mornings with a vicious north-easter howling through the streets and rattling ill-fitting window frames and front doors, a day when one hugged bed and wished humanity were as wise as animals that hibernated. In a word, we all had overslept. Panic on my sister's part as, grumbling, she rushed about knowing that she would be late for work. I heard the jaw-jaw between Mother and her from the comfort of my bed. There was no necessity on my part to race against the clock. To my pleasant surprise my sister planked a cup of tea on my bedside table together with a letter. 'I'll have to skedaddle,' she said. 'Mother forgot to set the alarm.' She rushed off.

The letter began:

Dear Sir,
    We will publish your novel ...

I sat up and bawled my sister's name. She came back at the double. 'Look!' I said and waved the letter. 'They've taken it.' She cried: 'Hooray', and shouted for Mother who, all eyes, came in combing her hair. 'Well, I never,' she said when I read the letter aloud. 'Oh, and what a tale I'll have to tell them at the café *this* morning.' She, too, hurried off. I sat there quite oblivious of the cold. I heard Mother's voice bidding me a good morning, then the door slammed. I listened to her joyful 'tra-la-laaing' as she sang her way up the street.

'We will publish your novel ...'

I was on the threshold of a wonderful year, though this I did not know.

# 45

# *The Man at Uncle's*

Bulldozers are at their work of destruction here. In this, the ward and parish of St Thomas, for the first time in a hundred years and more, daylight looks again on what once had been the green fields.

It has the face of a battlefield, this place, as though ruffian armies, besieging and besieged, had fought to the death for its possession. Street upon street of little houses, corner shops and pubs crashing into heaps of rubble. Bonfires of front doors, window frames and floorboards; funeral pyres as it were of an age that is no more. Where the wreckers have finished their work only the cobbled roadways and pavements remain to mark the streets which were our childhood playgrounds and where our homes had stood. They were built when the British Empire was at the pinnacle of its wealth and power, and they had sheltered defrauded generations for whom life had been an endless struggle both insulting and deprived.

Over three decades have passed since I stood on the threshold of what proved to be for me a wonderful year, decades that have witnessed another world war, the voluntary liquidation of the Empire and the establishment of a social revolution of which this demolition is but a local aspect.

The face of today soon will have obliterated all trace of yesterday—that is, in this cleared area which extends to less than a hundred acres. Already the builders are working alongside the wreckers. Steel skeletons of the multi-storied flats are rising gaunt above the sky-line, the world of tomorrow springing from the ruins of yesterday. When completed the old neighbourhood will have changed its ancient and local name of 'parish and ward' for 'precinct'. It will stand encompassed by, or be crowing over, the wards and parishes that remain, most of which are identical in appearance with what the one now smoking in ruin used to be. But these, too, are in their twilight days. The tales they have to tell of yesterday, like that unregarded sermon in stone on the road opposite the parish church, have no meaning for the young. This, Brindleheath Road, falls steeply. It is one of the old ways home from pits, mills, factories and railway sheds. Near its summit, in the pavement, half an arm's length from the house walls, is a shallow channel scuffed out over the years by the weary homeward plod of forgotten generations. Through the eyes of childhood I see the elderly among them using the window-sills as handrails and, for me, the channel is as eloquent of bygone days as are the grooves of chariot wheels along the Appian Way.

Although the streets of the other wards and parishes retain the face of that which has been destroyed, they house tenants with the modern, the mobile outlook. Owner-driven cars many of which, in company with other possessions, carry the invisible sign 'Not Paid For', stand parked outside front doors. Where people keep the rent, insurance books and papers are other books belonging to the family — passports, their pages stamped with continental entry permits to places where the sun shines. A sudden flowering; meritorious children of my contemporaries, now adult, are graduates of Oxbridge, Red-brick and the local school of Advanced Technology. Yesterday the Depression and lo! by a hop, skip and jump the Space Age and a Welfare State. A five-day, forty-hour week, holidays with pay, superannuation pension schemes, lunch vouchers and works' canteens; an inrush of immigrants to fill the rising tide of jobs going begging, and organized Labour in conference with employers on equal terms.

There was plenty of time for my appointment in Manchester. I decided to walk, or rather stroll, the two miles which had been my daily routine in the not-all-that-long-ago. And there was the thorn tree by the river with which I had played my harmless game when I had stood on the threshold of my wonderful year. How pleasing to pay it a sentimental visit.

On my way I saw, hanging from the angle-bracket outside a double-fronted shop, the trade sign of 'Uncle's', the three gilt balls. It seemed utterly out of place in these 'never-had-it-so-good' days. A section of the windows was given over to transistor radios, record players, TV sets and guitars for sale on deferred terms. These were backed with a display of long-playing records of 'pop' groups and teenage vocalists all 'sleeved' in dazzling photographic colour reproductions. A crowd of fashionably dressed and hair-styled youngsters of both sexes stood at the shop's open door listening to an idolized singer.

The shop's proprietor, a man in his late fifties or early sixties, said, when I asked him the state of business in the pawnbroking line: 'Mine, d'you mean?' He pushed aside the newspaper he was reading and smiled. 'Dead, that's if you don't count the mugs that come pawning to get money for casinos, Bingo and the betting shops.' He indicated the audience outside. 'How's that for size?' he asked. 'Five and a half million teenagers in the country and the computers've worked it out that each of 'em has an average of three pounds ten a week spending money to chuck away. Twenty million quid to burn — a week.' He waved his hand towards the stock shelves of records, the boxes of crippling shoes and racks of fashionable teen-age clothing. 'That's what it goes on. Then there's the ton-up cowboys. Three hundred quid for a motor bike on the never-never and think nothing of it. That's the way they look at it these days. Good for trade — and I'm not knockin' 'em. Tell you, if we'd've had the money when we

were their age we'd've done just the same. Though—,' he
paused and rubbed his cheek, thoughtfully. 'If you ask me,
this "Have now—pay later" lark's getting out of hand.
'T'isn't healthy. Things never are when they're made too
easy. As for pawnbroking, if you want to see what's put paid
to that round here—aye, and anywhere else if it comes to
that—just look in at any post office. Monday, paying out
National Assistance and Retired Army Allowances; Tuesday,
Family Allowances and Widows' Pensions; Wednesday, War
Disabled Pensions; Thursday, Retirement, Air Force and
Navy Pensions; Friday, Old Age Pensions for the seventies
and over. Talk about a revolution? Not half. And I hope it's
come to stay. But—' he knocked on the counter with a rigid
forefinger: '—those three brass balls are staying up where
they are. I'm no pessimist but I don't like the look of it.' He
gave his hobby horse its head and away it galloped. 'Fat
years and lean years, the swing of the pendulum, remember.
I'd feel easier if there was less of the big snatch all round, the
grab for capital appreciation, bigger and bigger profits and
the shout for more and more pay for less and less work. All
these unofficial strikes and argy-bargy about lines of demarca-
tion. And take a squint at that.' He tapped the newspaper's
entertainment advertisement columns: 'Half a page of clubs.
Bingo barmy. Casinos ... "Open at 9 p.m. Close at dawn."
And I'll say nothing at all about this drug-taking. Nay.' He
made a wry face as though he did not find any satisfaction in
his country's credit-worthiness. 'Then what?' He put the
edge of his hand over his eyebrows in the manner of a look-
out. 'Up to here in debt and we're forced to borrow by the
hundreds o' millions to stiffen the pound. *There's* a nice bit
of international pawnbroking for you. The world's going
crackers. We never learn. But like I've said, one thing *is*
certain, they're staying up there where they are, those brass
balls, just in case.'

He turned to serve a couple of the teenagers and I went to visit the thorn tree.

*Kirk Michael*
*Isle of Man*
*April* 1966